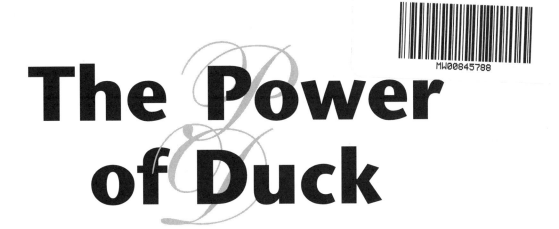

The Power of Duck

Integrated Rice and Duck Farming

Takao Furuno

Tagari Publications
Sisters Creek • Tasmania • Australia

A TAGARI PUBLICATION

First Edition 2001 A.D., 5000 print run

Illustrations: Janet Lane, after concept drawings by Takao Furuno and Tomoko Moriya

Photos: From prints supplied by Takao Furuno

Translators: Tony Boys, Puck Brecher, Tom Eskildsen

National Library of Australia Cataloguing-in-Publication

> Furuno, Takao
> The Power of Duck
>
> Includes index
> ISBN 0 908228 12 0
>
> 1. Agriculture
> 2. Environmental Studies

Cover design by: DiZign Pty Ltd, Lane Cove, NSW

Printed in Australia by STAR PRINTERY, Erskineville, NSW

Tagari Publications
Publishers for the Permaculture Institute since 1979
31 Rulla Road,
Sisters Creek, Tasmania 7325, Australia
Ph: 61 3 6445 0945
Fax: 61 3 6445 0944
Website: www.tagari.com

Foreword

One late autumn day in 1994, I departed for Hanoi, the capital of Vietnam. My objective was to participate in an international conference on the VAC method, which is an integrated farming method of Vietnam which organically combines fruit growing, stockbreeding and aquaculture.

The day before my departure, I bought a copy of Introduction to Permaculture (by Bill Mollison), which I happened to find in a bookstore in Japan.

I gave a presentation on my method of Integrated Rice and Duck Farming at the conference, with the cooperation of Japan International Volunteer Centre (JVC). The conference was a big success, with some 200 participants from different provinces of Vietnam as well as people from some 50 countries around the world.

The participants from Asia showed strong interest, but it seemed like the FAO staff and other westerners had trouble understanding my presentation.

Someone stepped up. "Good idea," he said in a friendly tone. It was none other than Bill Mollison, one of the originators of Permaculture! Until that moment, I hadn't even dreamed that he might be participating in the conference. Remembering that I had purchased his book just one day before my departure, I sensed something beyond coincidence. It was synchronicity, a glimpse of the mysterious interconnectedness of things.

Bill Mollison introduced Integrated Rice and Duck Farming in the Permaculture International Journal, and started showing an English video on the method at Permaculture courses.

In the late autumn of 1996, Bill came to Japan with his fiance Lisa. After giving lectures at the United Nations University and other places, they came all the way to visit our home. They spent a late autumn week here pulling daikon radishes, helping us deliver

With Bill Mollison in Hanoi

vegetables, playing with our five children, and getting a taste of small-scale organic farming as practised in Japan. We really hit it off well. That was when we decided to publish this book for our friends, the small-scale farmers of Asia.

It is interesting how people meet people.

Gassho*,
Takao Furuno

My wife Lisa, and I, first met Takao Furuno and his wife Tomiko in Hanoi in 1994, at a conference on domestic food security, attended by many Asian countries. We were very impressed with their illustrated talk on duck-rice farming, and wrote an account of it for the Permaculture Journal. We also arranged to later visit the Furuno family on a lecture tour to Japan, and worked as volunteers for a week, delivering eggs, poultry, miso, many vegetables, rice and news to 100 households in the nearby villages. The farm supplies most of their food needs. The Furunos also completed Permaculture training in Australia in 1998.

Foreword

We also visited villages in the mountains of Japan where many farms had adopted the duck-rice system, and drank too much hot sake! Subsequently, we visited duck-rice growers in Vietnam and Korea, and saw hundreds of hectares of this beneficial system. The Furuno family (there are 5 helpful children) are doing a great job in the extension of their system to all of Asia and Africa. By cooperating to produce "The Power of Duck", a title suggested by my daughter (Janet Lane) who also re-drew the figures after the concepts developed by Furuno and Tomoko Moriya, we hope to make the system available to English speakers.

After meeting, and staying with the Furuno family on their small farm (2ha) in Japan, and realising that their income from this farm (at about 130,000 Australian dollars annually) greatly exceeds that of many of the large farms (100 to 10,000ha) of Australia, I was very impressed. The farm is fully integrated, recycling wastes on site, and also fully organic. Fresh product (vegetables, rice, ducks, chicken and duck eggs) are sold directly to 100 consumer families, delivered to the door once or twice a week.

Consumers (mailmen, policemen, teachers) often drop by to help on the farm, and consumers and farmers are aware of each other's family birthdays, state of health, and welfare. It is a very human system, not subject to market fluctuations and intercontinental trade. Here, we can expect trade in information, for (like ourselves) the Furuno family travel and teach. One of my books is translated into Japanese; this present book is Furuno's gift to English speakers.

Takao Furuno never ceases to improve and teach his duck-rice (natural) farming system, and as it spreads village to village he has built up a body of 10,000 practitioners in Japan.

As well, the practice has been taught by Mr Furuno in Vietnam, Thailand, Korea, China, Taiwan and Indonesia, as well as Tanzania in Africa.

He has, in recent years, developed a duck tractor system that prepares last years' paddy field. About 3 weeks before planting, the field is flooded to 5cm, and ducks of any age (large and small) are turned in to remove all weeds. The large ducks are removed, and the field planted to rice seedlings, then the small ducks are returned (3 days to 3 weeks old) as rice cultivators.

He notes that ducks from 1 to 5 days are very useful in market garden pest control, as they are primarily insectivorous. Like some Thai farmers, Mr Furuno uses Azolla, a floating fern that scavenges nitrogen. This is "staged up" from a few glasshouse tanks, to a few open tanks, and then each paddy field gets a netted release of one are which is one hundredth of a hectare until it fills up. When the fence is removed the Azolla spreads right across the field. Wet weight yields of Azolla are about 30,000 kg/ha, and both mulch and nitrogen help the rice crop and the soil.

After the Azolla release, and the water is muddied by ducklings, he puts in small loach, who further forage insects and snails, and who like to reproduce in muddied water. These are easily recovered from small ponds dug in the fields as they are drained, and can be kept in the winter pond until next season. The ducks will eat loach in clear water, but mud and Azolla protect them in planted fields.

Azolla and duck, loach and shield shrimp all add nutrients for the crop.

If I understand Furuno, his passion is for the preservation and health of the small family farm, from which we all originally came, but which is greatly threatened by the "get big or get out" syndrome. He has shown the small farm to be not just a very healthy lifestyle, which assists environmental and social health, but a rich life for his whole family.

The way of thinking, the <u>thoughtfulness</u> of this farm evolution (and this is a farm carried on the back of a duck!) is wonderful, you will agree with me when you read Furuno's modest prose. He is, in my terms, duck-tractoring, just like many of us chicken-tractor, and some of us pig-tractor. Our livestock are our labour force and manure factory. In Egypt, farmers build palaces for pigeons, and reap a manure crop. Furuno lets his ducks walk in his fields, and his loaches swim in them as well, as manure spreaders.

What Furuno does with ducks, several of my students have achieved with geese and hens, as cultivators and weeders in a cycle of dryland vegetables. It is no longer possible to pretend that the chemical "farming" is either necessary or productive, nor do people want to eat such products. So, forward to a future, marvellously powered by chickens and ducks!

It is with pride and hope therefore, that we publish this book, as a thoroughly-described and very well-tried system of sustainable, productive, clean polyculture in paddy fields, applicable everywhere paddy rice is grown. It serves as a text book for case studies and farmer-evolved natural systems.

The Furuno family and ourselves both self-fund overseas teaching visits to small farms, and deeply believe in the benefits of productive, small, natural farms.

We (my wife and I) believe that reading this book will be a rich reference for Permaculture teachers, and that they can integrate the system in their teaching, internationally, we are grateful to the Furuno family and the interpreters - especially to Tom. Aigamo Banzai!

Bill and Lisa Mollison
Farmers and Publishers
Tagari Publications
Tasmania, Australia
Phone   61 3 6445 9045
Fax   61 3 6445 0944
Website: www.tagari.com

Profits from Tagari Publications support the Permaculture Institute in its global activities. We publish books on agricultural systems, and on Permaculture.

Publishers' Clarifications:

KEY TO ABBREVIATIONS

a = one are = 1/100 hectare, or 10 x 10 m (100 square metres). A hectare is 10,000m^2 or 100 x 100m. It is 2.471 acres. One metres is 39.4 inches. See pg 16 - taubo 3.3m^2
J = Japanese language, or name.

DUCK BREED

The Aigamo duck, a small breed, is a cross between small Mallard drakes, and Khaki Campbell ducks, or duck of a lighter breed.
Yields (p41 et. seq.) of sifted brown rice are 513 kg/10a, or 5,130kg/ha.

Contents

Duck Song

BÀI CA LÚA - VỊT
Duck - Rice song
Tanbo no Ahiru San

Music & Lyrics : ĐOÀN NHÂN ÁI
Japanese Lyrics : SUZUKI AKIKO

Chapter One

The Theory of Integrated Rice and Duck Farming

I. Introduction

My family farms a small plot of land in Japan. We currently have 2 ha of farmland, of which we use 1.4 ha for Integrated Rice and Duck Farming and 0.6 ha for growing pesticide-free vegetables. We have a teikei (direct tie-up) with about 100 households of consumers.

I started organic farming in 1977. In 1987 I began practising Integrated Rice and Duck Farming.

For the first ten years until I encountered the Aigamo Duck (which is a cross between a wild and a domesticated duck) , I got up every morning before dawn and spent the whole day weeding our paddy fields under the burning sun. Since I had experienced these ten years of hardship, I became totally fascinated with the Aigamo duck from the moment of our first encounter. I have devoted the last twelve years since then to practical research on Integrated Rice and Duck Farming.

If one goes to rice-growing areas in Asia, one almost always finds ducks. Rice paddies and ducks (waterfowl) have a close, inseparable relationship. However, it seems that ducks are generally underrated everywhere. In Japan there is the expression "a sitting duck". In Vietnam people say "if you want to be rich, raise fish; if you want to make good money, raise pigs; if you want to be poor, raise ducks.' However, if commonplace ducks and rice plants are brought together in an enclosed paddy field to do Integrated Rice and Duck Farming, one will see how wrong this evaluation is. We need to reassess our relationship with ducks.

My sincere wish is that this book will be helpful for small farming families in Asia, Africa, and around the world.

II. What is Integrated Rice and Duck Farming? (The basic idea)

What is Integrated Rice and Duck Farming? I intend to answer this question in this book. Here I would like to give a simple definition of this term as a starting point for common understanding. The Aigamo Duck is a cross-breed of a wild male duck and a domesticated female duck. I have been using the Aigamo Duck in my paddy fields because it is hardy, tastes good, and works well. I think it would be best for the readers to use native ducks of your country or region.

Aigamo Ducks

Geese

Aigamo Ducks Swimming in the Paddy Fields

Muscovy Ducks

Domesticated waterfowl can be broadly classified into three categories: common ducks, geese, and Muscovy ducks. Of these, Muscovy ducks are weak to water so they are not suitable for Integrated Rice and Duck Farming. Neither are geese, as they eat the leaves of the rice plant. Native ducks of a somewhat small size are best. My comprehensive technique of Integrated Rice and Duck Farming is carried out as follows:

a. The paddy field is enclosed using a bamboo fence, a net, an electric fence, or other available materials. This enclosure is used to protect the ducks from predators, and to prevent them from escaping.

b. 1-2 weeks after transplanting of the rice seedlings, small ducklings that are about 1-2 weeks old are released in the paddy field, in a proportion of 20 - 30 ducklings per 10 are.

c. The ducklings are raised in the paddy fields both day and night until the rice ears are formed (in Japan, about 2-3 months). They are not just released in the paddy fields in the daytime and taken out at night, as is often the case in Asian villages. Of course, it is perhaps inevitable that the ducks have to be brought home at night in

some Asian countries if they are liable to be stolen.

In your country, what is the traditional method for releasing ducks in the paddy field? Is it the same method, or different?

Method of Enclosure:-

Figure 1 – Net or Electric Fence

As a test, try releasing Aigamo ducklings in a paddy field after transplanting the rice seedlings. The ducklings will swim all around the paddy field, voraciously eating the weeds, insects, frogs, tadpoles, and mud in the paddy field. They will grow in leaps and bounds. The rice plants will tiller, branch out, and grow vigorously.

The Aigamo ducks will eat the rice ears once they have formed. However, until then, they will hardly eat any rice leaves, even though they will eat many weeds. This mechanism is truly a blessing of nature.

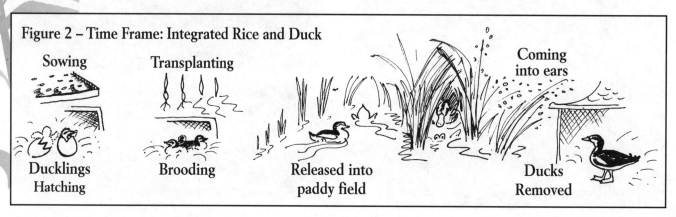

Figure 2 – Time Frame: Integrated Rice and Duck

Sowing   Transplanting   Coming into ears

Ducklings Hatching   Brooding   Released into paddy field   Ducks Removed

The moment that the Aigamo ducks are released in the paddy field, they begin to work, converting the once troublesome weeds and pests into duck food, i.e., resources. The duck manure provides nutrients to the rice as well. In other words, with this method, the more weeds (food) in the paddy field, the better!

The Aigamo ducks are given only a very small amount of feed, mainly to establish communication with them. The ducks and the rice flourish together, using only the resources within the paddy field. This is what I call Integrated Rice and Duck Farming.

1. A Comprehensive Technique (Integrated Rice and Duck Farming is not merely a weeding technique)

Releasing waterfowl in the paddy field is a very simple matter. However, the significance of this has varied greatly depending on the person, the country and the times. This is both interesting and important. There are still quite a few people who consider the Aigamo duck as merely a means for weeding. In my comprehensive technique of Integrated Rice and Duck Farming, the paddy field is enclosed using an electric fence, net, etc., to create an environment in which the Aigamo ducks and rice can prosper symbiotically. This relationship between the Aigamo ducks, the rice plants, and the paddy field is described in Figure 3. I call this "the World of One Duck-Myriad Blessings."

The ducks are an end as well as a means. Rice farming and stock breeding have been integrated organically in the paddy field.

As can be seen from Figure 3, the ducks have the following six combined effects on the rice: 1. Weeding Effect, 2. Pest Control Effect, 3. Manuring Effect, 4. Full-time Ploughing & Muddying Effect, 5. Golden Snail Control Effect, 6. Rice Stimulation Effect.

On the other hand, the paddy field has benefits for the ducks such as the following: 1. utilization of unused resources such as weeds, insects, and water plants, as food; 2. utilization of unused space in the paddy field as duck habitat; 3. abundant water; 4. places for the ducks to hide under the rice leaves.

In recent years, this system is becoming even more diverse and creative through addition of fish and azolla, a nitrogen-fixing water plant.

2. The Idea makes all the difference (Weeds and Insects exist for the sake of the Rice Plants)

Nothing is without significance in nature. All things perform the roles that they have been given in the ecosystems of this planet.

Figure 3 – "The World of One Duck-Myriad Blessings" = The Duck Effect

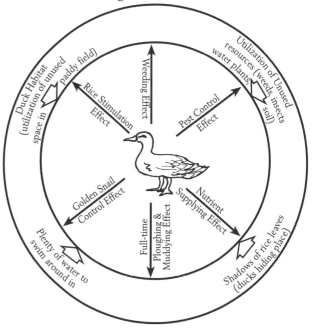

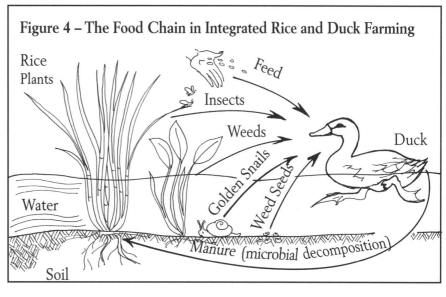

Figure 4 – The Food Chain in Integrated Rice and Duck Farming

This is absolutely true regarding weeds and pests in the paddy field as well. However, in modernized rice farming, the relationship between humans and the rice plant has been over emphasized so much that these "weeds" and "pests" are judged as merely "harmful"... and a "nuisance." They have been exterminated (controlled) using herbicides and pesticides.

However, the situation changes completely once the ducks are released in the paddy fields. Our "fixed ideas" are immediately disproven. Interestingly, the insects and weeds which we had thought were "bad guys" become precious food for the ducks, and are converted into blood and flesh, nutrients for the rice plants, and finally, the rice and meat dishes that we eat.

An agricultural extension worker once said to me "Mr. Furuno, you have reduced the weeds so much by raising the ducks in your paddy field, that you will have to sow weed seeds next year, won't you!"

He said this as a joke, but in later years, what he said came true. This technique does have a slight contradiction. Four or five weeks after releasing the ducks in the paddy field, the number of weeds and insects is noticeably reduced as a result of the "duck effect. "This is a natural and desired effect. However, this also results in a decrease in the natural supply of duck feed in the paddy field.

So, with a further reversal in thinking, I began to grow a water "weed "called azolla as a "fodder crop" in the paddy field, to feed the ducks. In other words, I actively introduced weeds into the paddy field. Perhaps you could call this a reversal of a reversal in thinking.

Aigamo Duck with Azolla

3. That which Is Old is Truly New (Comparison with Modernized Rice Farming)

Integrated Rice and Duck Farming is not a totally new technique; it is a rediscovery and rebuilding of a traditional technique. This becomes clear when we compare it with modernized techniques. As shown in Figure 5, modernized rice farming has used a single method to address each problem, with application of herbicides to weeds, pesticides or agrichemicals to pests or diseases, and chemical fertilizers to provide soil nutrients. It takes a "Band Aid" approach, treating symptoms one by one. However, the duck performs all of these roles by itself. This is the key to the comprehensive technique of "One Duck-Myriad Blessings."

4. What it means to Work (Liberation Stockbreeding)

In conventional farming, no matter how convenient the pesticides, herbicides and chemical fertilizers are, they must be used as external inputs.

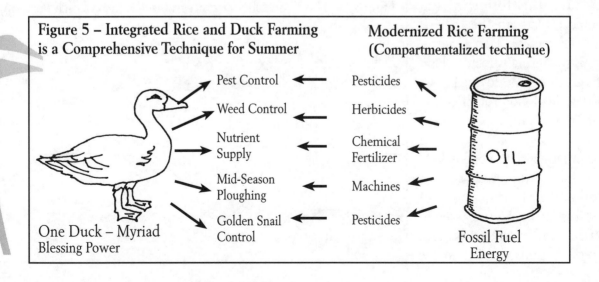

Figure 5 – Integrated Rice and Duck Farming is a Comprehensive Technique for Summer

Modernized Rice Farming (Compartmentalized technique)

One Duck – Myriad Blessing Power

Pest Control	←	Pesticides
Weed Control	←	Herbicides
Nutrient Supply	←	Chemical Fertilizer
Mid-Season Ploughing	←	Machines
Golden Snail Control	←	Pesticides

OIL

Fossil Fuel Energy

Someone must spray them on the field. Even if they are sprayed using a machine, someone needs to drive the machine.

However, in Integrated Rice and Duck Farming, the ducks in the paddy field do all of the weeding, pest control, and fertilizing. There is no need for meticulous management or excessive labor inputs. That is why the duck can be called a "working animal". Yet, it is totally different from working animals such as horses that pull heavy loads or oxen that toil under the hot sun, ploughing the paddy fields.

Horses and oxen work laboriously in the fields, but ducks do their work merely by eating, playing, defecating and sleeping, as they please. The ducks as well as the rice grow naturally as a result. The ducks are not "working" as such; they are moving about freely and happily. Perhaps you could say that the ducks are "happy working animals."

Compare the ducks, which can play and forage freely in the spacious paddy field, with broilers cooped up in a windless chicken house. I refer to Integrated Rice and Duck Farming as "liberation stockbreeding."

The duck not only works, but also manures the field and performs many roles. Integrated Rice and Duck Farming is an enjoyable and distinctly Asian stockbreeding method that utilises the full potential of the livestock.

5. The Potential for Cyclic Sustainability

i. Modernized Rice Farming Creates an Impoverished System

By mid-June, one can enjoy the beautiful scenery of paddy fields throughout Japan. In orthodox organic vegetable growing, crop rotation, field rotation and mixed cropping are used to grow a wide variety of vegetables in order to minimize the occurrence of weeds, pests, and diseases. But in the case of modernized rice farming, which focuses only on short-term production with minimum labor, as well as in the case of organic rice farms, only one crop is planted. [Modernized rice farming in Japan is a monoculture system with a one-year cycle.]

It is said in ecology that ecosystems undergo succession (evolution) from a state of high productivity to a state of equilibrium. Agriculture uses a certain input of human "work" to artificially block the evolution of the ecosystem and to reap a harvest from a simplified system which maximizes the growth of only certain crops. Thus, it is the natural (diversifying) tendency of ecological succession (i.e., evolution) for weeds or pests to appear in a paddy field planted only with rice. In Japanese modernized rice farming, pesticides and herbicides are sprayed in order to block natural succession and maximize production. The ecosystem of the paddy field thus becomes even more simplified and impoverished.

ii. Creative Diversification

By releasing ducks into the rice monoculture, one can increase diversity while controlling the growth (i.e. , diversification) of weeds and pests. One can create a new, diverse ecosystem where rice, ducks, and water plants coexist. This is what I aim for in Integrated Rice and Duck Farming. Since 1993, I have attempted to further increase diversity by introducing azolla, a nitrogen-fixing aquatic fern, to the duck-paddy field. What is very interesting and exciting about Integrated Rice and Duck Farming is that creatively increasing diversity can increase productivity rather than reduce it.

iii. Rice Farming as a Permanent Cycle

In order to clearly show the characteristics of Integrated Rice and Duck Farming, I would like to schematically compare the material cycles of "modernized rice farming, " "organic rice farming," "Integrated Rice and Duck Farming," and "Integrated Rice, Duck, and Azolla Farming." The development of modernized rice farming was a process of substituting human labor with massive amounts of imported fossil fuel energy and other external inputs.

So-called organic rice farming directly causes relatively little pollution, since it does not use industrially produced chemical fertilizers or agrichemicals. However, Japan is deeply dependent upon overseas sources for its raw materials for compost and organic fertilizer. It could be said that organic rice growing in Japan is based upon the fertility of American (overseas) soil. However, in the case of Integrated Rice and Duck Farming, the only external input to the paddy field is, as a rule, a small quantity of rice screenings which are fed to the ducks. The weeds and insects eaten by the ducks become nutrients, and the "duck effect" promotes the growth of the rice plants. Integrated Rice and Duck Farming is clearly more permanent and cyclical than the other methods.

The Integrated Rice, Duck, and Azolla farming Method is an even more creative way of establishing a permanent productive cycle. In figure 6 the description of the four cycles is of course only schematic; in practice, there are many variations. For instance, there are quite a few people who add compost to their duck-paddy fields.

6. The Diverse Productivity of the Paddy Field (Is a paddy field just for growing rice?)

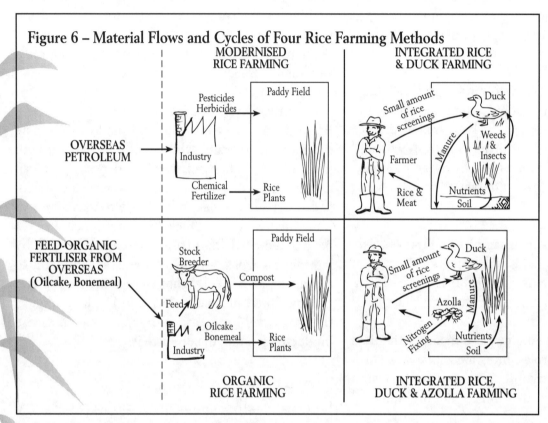

Figure 6 – Material Flows and Cycles of Four Rice Farming Methods

Figure 7 - The Diverse Productivity of the Paddy Field

= RICE = R
= DUCK = D
= FISH = F
= AZOLLA = A

In our long history of rice-growing, we Japanese have been too spellbound by the idea that "the paddy field is a place just for growing rice". So-called modernization of agriculture and rice farming was also fixated with this idea. In contrast, my technique of Integrated Rice and Duck Farming Method is a delightful experiment in simultaneous rice growing and stock-breeding in a paddy field. It goes the opposite direction of modernized farming techniques, which have continued to become more specialized and symptom-oriented. Thanks to our friend the duck, we have been able to rediscover the diverse productive power of the paddy field.

In paddy fields throughout the rest of Asia, fish and shrimp have been grown together with rice, providing an important daily food source for people and making the most of the paddy field's intrinsically diverse productive potential. The question is whether we notice this potential and incorporate it in our farming technique.

I have actively tried to technically incorporate this diverse productive potential into my recently developed Integrated Rice, Duck, Azolla and Fish Farming Method. It is a technique to establish a permanent cycle for rice growing, stockbreeding and aquaculture, by creating a new ecosystem of ducks, azolla, rice plants, fish, weeds, insects, etc., in the paddy field. The paddy field becomes a place to produce not only rice, but the side-dishes as well.

7. The Significance of Integrated Rice and Duck Farming as a Farming Method

Western agriculture is said to have developed in stages from the Three Phase Method to the Grain-Grass Method, and then to the Rotational Cultivation Method. Fallows were discontinued, perennial grasses, red clover and root vegetables (turnips) were grown on arable land to increase the supply of fodder, grazing was replaced by stockbreeding in feed lots, and the resulting compost was returned to the crops. A system for restoring and increasing soil fertility was established through a skilful combination of crop varieties and stockbreeding, whereby an increase in fodder crops led to increased livestock production, increased compost production, and increased production of crops.

Table 1 – The Agricultural Revolution in the West		
Agricultural Revolution	Fertility Maintenance System	more fodder crops -> increased livestock production -> more compost -> increased crop production
	Weed Control System:	row planting by animal power + deep ploughing in summer -> weed control by animal power

Table 2 – Japanese Agriculture-Unchanged for Two Thousand Years		
Traditional Japanese Agriculture	Fertility Maintenance System	grass from the mountains + night soil
	Weed Control System:	manual weeding
Modern Rice Farming	Fertility Maintenance System	chemical fertilizers
	Weed Control System:	herbicides

This also resulted in a weed control system based on row-planting and weeding with animal power, deep ploughing for root vegetables in the summertime, etc.

On the other hand, Japanese agriculture has long depended upon grasses from outside of the farmlands for maintaining soil fertility. Grass was cut and carried in by human or animal power, mixed with night soil, and added to the fields. Weed control was done mostly by hand. The gruelling work of weeding the paddy fields under the hot summer sun was typical. The basic tendency to rely on external inputs has not changed till today-modernizing has simply replaced grass with chemical fertilizers and hand-weeding with herbicides. In its two thousand year history, Japanese agriculture never underwent a transformation in farming methods such as the "agricultural revolution" in the West.

How about Integrated Rice and Duck Farming? East Asian agriculture is often said to be "animal-less" agriculture [based almost solely on human labor]. However, Integrated Rice and Duck Farming is a very "animal-full" farming method, combining rice growing with stockbreeding.

One distinct feature of the method is the place where the animals are kept. In the Three Phase Method and the Grain-Grass Method, the livestock graze on the fallows or pasture, while with the Rotational Cultivation Method, they are kept in a feed lot.

Table 3 – Integrated Rice and Duck Farming as an Agricultural Method		
Integrated Rice and Duck Farming	Fertility Maintenance System	The ducks eat the weeds, pests and azolla; manure provides nutrients.
	Weed Control System:	duck weeding effect

However, in Integrated Rice and Duck Farming, the animals (ducks) are raised right in the farmland (paddy field) in which the grain crop is growing. It is clearly different from Western stockbreeding in this respect.

The system for maintaining soil fertility in Integrated Rice and Duck Farming is also unique. The weeds and pests, which would normally be a nuisance, become feed for the ducks, whose manure provides nutrients for the rice plants. Azolla, which is an aquatic fodder crop, can also be grown among the rice plants. The ducks eat the azolla and convert it into nutrients for the rice plants.

The weeding is done by duck-power. Duck-power weeding also maintains the fertility of the soil. This is a creative synthesis of rice farming and stockbreeding in common space-time, evolved from the legacy of traditional Asian agriculture.

Stockbreeding and rice growing are done at the same time and place.

Nowadays, the world is paying much attention to "environmentally appropriate agriculture," "sustainable agriculture," and "organic farming". However, the basic issue is not the often-mentioned dependency of modernized agriculture on excessive use of pesticides, chemical fertilizers and herbicides, so much as it is the very "lack of method" in agriculture.

It is really interesting to take a second look at traditional Asian agriculture and Integrated Rice and Duck Farming from the perspective of agricultural method.

8. Technical Position

Compared to "Reduced Agrichemical Farming," in which a certain amount of pesticides, chemical fertilizer, and herbicides is used, true organic farming has always required generous inputs of human labor to improve the soil and control weeds, etc. However, the process of modernization of agriculture in Japan during the last 50 years since World War II has been a process of labor saving through substitution of human labor with fossil fuel energy. This is one of the main reasons that organic farming has not spread widely, even though it is known to be good for the environment and to yield wholesome, delicious produce. The image that most people have of true organic farming in Japan is that it requires such hard work that only people with a deep sense of commitment are able to do it.

Integrated Rice and Duck Farming is one approach to organic farming, but it is a bit different. This is because it makes full use of the amphibious capabilities of waterfowl, something which has been totally forgotten in Japanese agriculture in recent years. It allows creative utilization of animal power. Usage of energy has shifted from human power to animal power, and then to fossil fuel energy. Nowadays, fossil fuel energy is used for just about everything, but there is still much interesting potential for the use of animal power. In Integrated Rice and Duck Farming, the ducks complete the farmwork by freely feeding and playing in the paddy field, growing together with the rice.

In conventional organic farming, it has been said "You must persevere 5 to 10 years for the soil to become fertile, natural pest-predators to increase, and weed seeds to diminish. Only then will you get good soil in which anything grows." But any highly motivated person anywhere can apply the Integrated Rice and Duck Farming Method with moderate success even from the first year. This means that it may be technically possible for agrichemical-free rice farming to become the standard way of growing rice, rather than something out of the ordinary.

9. A Participatory Technology

As explained above, Integrated Rice and Duck Farming is a technique utilizing some very interesting mechanisms. It is a technique that is developed creatively by the farmer her/himself.

Modernized agricultural technology in Japan has generally been developed by companies, universities or agricultural experiment stations, and has been widely accepted due to promotion by agricultural extension centers, agricultural cooperatives, or companies. It seems very convenient, but it is a technology based totally on external resources which are not produced on the farm.

Weeding in Vietnam

It is a passive, highly controlled and "do according to the manual" type technology in which the farmer has no creative involvement.

In contrast, Integrated Rice and Duck Farming is a "participatory technology" developed by the farmer her/himself through a creative combination of ducks, rice plants and other things in or around the farm, so that they work together best under the natural, economic and social conditions of the locality. Integrated Rice and Duck Farming is "farmer's technology." It lets you be yourself.

10. A Technique Common to Asia

Since 1992, I have had the opportunity to travel through the rural areas of various Asian countries such as China, Taiwan, South Korea, Indonesia, Vietnam, Malaysia, Cambodia and the Philippines. What one sees in the villages of Asia is quite similar from country to country. Barefoot farmers plough their small plots of land using oxen or water buffaloes. The rice seedlings are transplanted by hand. Weeding is done by hand. Harvesting is also done manually. Many people can be seen actively working in the paddy fields. But such traditional farming is gradually changing as chemical fertilizers and agrichemicals are starting to be used. This is the general situation of Asian villages, which are being rapidly drawn into the market economy in recent years. Nowadays, Integrated Rice and Duck Farming is quietly spreading throughout Asia, particularly South Korea and Vietnam.

In Asian developing countries, the cost of chemical fertilizers and agrichemicals is relatively high compared to the price of rice. In general, farmers laboriously weed by hand, just as I used to. So it would be relatively easy to switch to Integrated Rice and Duck Farming.

Present-day Japanese agriculture is high-input agriculture that is totally dependent upon external inputs. It is doubtful that a resource-poor country like Japan will be able to continue such high-input type agriculture in the 21st century, when the world's population will exceed 10 billion and a global food crisis is certain to come. It will also be difficult for agriculture in all Asian countries to be modernized in the way that Japanese agriculture has, due to the limitations of our planet's resources, energy, and

environmental carrying capacity. The only reason that modernized agriculture can continue is that its use is limited mostly to the industrially developed countries.

What must be done? There is only one choice - "alternative modernization" of agriculture that benefits both developing and developed countries. Integrated Rice and Duck Farming is one of the solutions.

III. *The Behaviour of Ducks*

1. The Duck is a Hard Worker

Generally speaking, there are two approaches to raising ducks in the paddy field.

a. the daytime-only approach
The ducks are released in the paddy field in the daytime, but are kept in a shed, etc., at night.
b. the 24 hour approach
The ducks are kept in the paddy field day and night.

According to my findings, duck raising in paddy fields in Asia almost always follows the daytime-only approach. In contrast, in my Integrated Rice and Duck Farming Method, the ducks are as a rule kept in the paddy field both day and night, 24 hours a day. This is because ducks, unlike chickens, have night vision, and are able to feed both day and night. They feed most actively from late night until early morning. In the daytime, wild ducks normally stay afloat in the middle of the lake or pond, where it is safe. This is known as the "duck's floating nap" in Japan. They go to feed in the paddy fields and shallow ponds mainly from night until early morning.

The duck is a hard worker, and work around the clock. I have often seen them foraging in the moonlight.

The effectiveness of Integrated Rice and Duck Farming would be halved if the daytime-only approach were used. The trouble of taking the ducks to and from the paddy field every day would also limit the area of implementation.

That is why Integrated Rice and Duck Farming calls for keeping the ducks in the paddy fields day and night.

Table 4 – The Ducks' Weeding Effect (types and dry weight of weeds per square meter)							
Resodia; Weeds g/m²							
plot	Barnyard Millet (E) Inu-bie (J)	Kishu-suzumeno-hie (J) *Paspalum Distel chum* knot grass (E)	Umbrella Plant *Cyperus serotinas* Mizugayaisuti (J)	*Lindernia procumbens* Azena (J)	*Rotala indica* Kikashigasa (J)	*Monochoria vaginalis* Duck tongue weed Konagi (J)	algae Mo (J)!HL
Duck plot	8.1	0.03	0.05	0.04	1.32	0.15	4.28
Control plot	12.4	0.9	0.28	0.1	0.85	60.7	10.2

2. Ducks usually eat the ears of rice, but not the rice leaves.

The workings of nature are remarkable. It seems as if the duck evolved for the purpose of rice cultivation. Ducks happily eat soft weeds and rice ears, but not rice leaves. When the ducklings are first released into the paddy field, both they and the rice seedlings are quite small. However, the ducklings normally do not eat the rice plant's leaves, which are rich in silica and feel hard and rough. However, if a large number of over-sized ducks are released in a newly transplanted paddy field, they sometimes eat the tips of the rice leaves. In such cases, there is an imbalance between the ducks and the rice plants.

IV. The Duck Effect and Its Mechanisms

I would now like to explain the effect of releasing ducks in the paddy field, and its mechanism, in more detail, using data wherever possible. As shown in Figure 3 on p.9, the "duck effect" consists of the following:

1. weeding effect.
2. pest control effect.
3. nutrient supplying effect.
4. full-time ploughing and muddying effect.
5. golden snail control effect.
6. rice stimulation effect.

Inside the control plot.

In some Asian countries such as Vietnam and Laos, it is reported that ducks also help to control rats and crabs that damage the rice seedlings.

The Concept of "Control" by Ducks

Weeds and pests are reduced noticeably when ducks are released into the paddy field. This is normally referred to as the weeding effect and pest control effect of ducks. However, this doesn't seem quite the right expression.

Pesticides and herbicides annihilate weeds and insects. In this case, it may be appropriate to speak of "control" of pests and weeds, as one is actively trying to suppress and

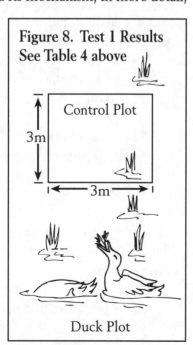

Figure 8. Test 1 Results See Table 4 above

Control Plot
3m
3m
Duck Plot

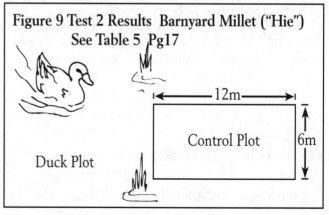

Figure 9 Test 2 Results Barnyard Millet ("Hie") See Table 5 Pg17

Duck Plot
12m
Control Plot
6m

eliminate them. However, in Integrated Rice and Duck Farming, the weeds and insects provide feed for the ducks and nutrients for the rice plants - they are used as resources. This is "utilization" rather than "control." We could say that the duck is a "companion animal" to the rice, in the same way that we speak of "companion plants." Ducks utilize the weeds and insects rather than merely control them in the way the pesticides and herbicides do. There is a need for a new concept to replace that of "control." I haven't been able to think of an alternative term, so I will tentatively use the term "control," but please understand it to mean "utilization."

1. The Weeding Effect

The weeding effect is one of the most important and easily understood aspects of the "duck effect." I have noticed that the total amount of weeds in my paddy fields is much less than that in nearby paddy fields in which herbicides are being used. I spent ten years hand-weeding my paddy fields, so I really know how helpful the ducks' weeding effect is.

45 Aigamo ducklings were released into a 28 a test plot on July 1st. Seedlings of the rice variety "Hinohikari" had been transplanted on June 13th at a density of 45 hills per *tsubo* (3.3 square meters).

As shown in Figure 8, a control plot was made inside the test plot, and the two plots were compared. Table 4 shows a comparison of the types and quantities of weeds per square meter. In the test plot, the quantity of duck tongue weed *(Monochoria vaginalis)*, one of the most high priority weeds, was found to be 1/500 of that in the control plot. The weeding effect is obvious.

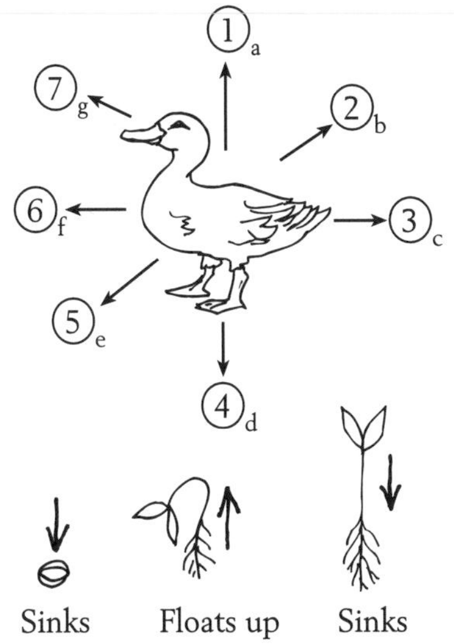

Table 5 – Test 2 Results	
	Number of Barnyard Millet plants
Duck Plot	7
Control Plot	212

Layout of the Paddy Field

Duck Plot
Control Plot: (12 m x 6 m)
Area: 28 a
Rice variety: "Ougonbare"
Transplanting: 8 June
Ducklings released: 30 June
Number of ducklings: 75
Day of investigation: 11 Sept. 1992

Investigator: Mr. Motoyasu Noai, Kaho Agricultural Improvement/Extension Center
Method: the number of barnyard millet plants in an area of 6 m x 6 m in the duck plot and the control plot was counted.

Table 5 shows the results of an investigation concerning barnyard millet. It shows that ducks are very effective in controlling barnyard grass.*

(Translator's note: There are three main types of barnyard millet (Japanese: hie or nobie) that grow in Japanese paddy fields: inubie (Echinochloa crus-galli Beauv.), tainubie (Echinochloa crus-galli Beauv. var. oryzicola Ohwi) and himetainubie (Echinochloa crus-galli Beauv. var. formosensis Ohwi). "Barnyard millet" refers to a combination of any of these, unless otherwise indicated. Barnyard millet is to be distinguished from cultivated millet, Echinochloa frumentacea.

i. The Mechanism of Weed Control by Ducks
When ducks are released in the paddy field, the weeds eventually disappear. The weeding effect is obvious.

However, it is still not well understood why the weeds disappear. It seems that the mechanism is not so simple. In fact, it is quite complex. Our observations lead us to infer that there are seven reasons for the

Figure 10 The Mechanism of Weed Control with Ducks

Sinks   Floats up   Sinks

weeding effect, as shown in Figure 10. It is very important to understand these seven reasons and to keep them in mind when implementing this method.

    a. The ducks eat the weeds.

    b. The ducks eat the weed seeds in the mud.

    c. Churning the muddy water with their bills and feet, the ducks cause the germinating weed seeds to float to the surface, and the ungerminated seeds to sink into the mud.

    d. The ducks step on the weeds, sinking them into the mud.

    e. The full-time plowing and muddying effect reduces the intensity of sunlight in the water, hindering photosynthesis of the weeds.

    f. Increased turbidity due to mixing of the ducks' manure with the muddy water hinders the germination of the weed seeds.

    g. Oxygen gas rises out of the water due to the churning action of the ducks' bills and feet, causing chemical reduction which inhibits germination of the weeds.

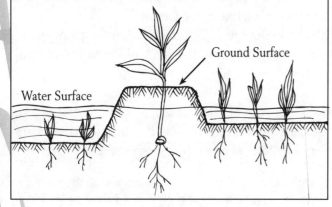

Figure 11 – Weeds grow profusely with deep roots in shallow water and on islands

ii. Conditions for Weed Control

With an understanding of the mechanism of interaction between ducks and weeds, let us attempt to put together a technique for weed control, taking into consideration the state of the paddy field, the growth condition of weeds, rearing of the ducks, and other relevant conditions.

    a. Leveling the surface of the paddy field

No matter how well the ducks perform, barnyard millet and other weeds grow profusely on islands or in shallow places in the paddy field. Weeds grow well on islands or in shallow areas because they have plenty of oxygen

and the right amount of moisture. "The growth of weeds in soil under water is 1/3 of that in wet soil saturated with water, and 1/6 of that in a garden or field. There is a particularly major reduction in C4 type weeds (such as barnyard millet and crabgrass), which compete with the rice plant."

(Note: Plants can be classified as C3 type plants and C4 type plants, whose chemical paths for fixing carbon dioxide by photosynthesis are different. C4 type plants have higher photosynthetic capability and tend to grow more vigorously than C3 type plants when sunlight is strong. Rice is a C3 type plant, so it is weak in competition with C4 type weeds.)

Furthermore, weeds in shallow water or on an island grow from deeper down in the soil than weeds in deep water. That is why they are not easily uprooted even if the ducks churn them with their bills and feet.

Testing weed growth at different water depths in PET bottles.

Normally, waterfowl will mix food with water and slush it around in their bills, spitting out what is unneeded. However, ducks are unable to perform this typical feeding activity on an island in the paddy field, due to lack of water.

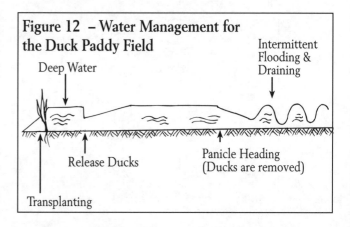

Figure 12 – Water Management for the Duck Paddy Field

If the soil dries up and hardens even once, the ducks will no longer be able to easily uproot the weeds with their bills or feet, even if the soil is submerged again. So the first key to success in weed control is to do a very thorough job of puddling and leveling the paddy field, so that it is very flat and has no shallow areas or islands.

b. Water Management

During the two weeks or so between transplantation of rice seedlings and release of the ducklings, the water in the paddy field is kept as deep as possible in order to control the growth of weeds. In weed germination tests done using soil from my paddy field, it was found that barnyard millet can hardly germinate if the water depth is 13 cm or more. In water that is 10 cm deep or more, even if the weeds can germinate, they become very thin and weak, and cannot grow well.

However, the optimum water depth after the ducklings have been released in the paddy field is such that they can float and swim on the water, as well as walk around, i.e., their feet can just barely touch the soil. If the water is too deep for the ducks' feet or bills to touch the bottom, the water does not become muddy, and the full effect of the ducks is not achieved. In this case, Duck tongue weed (*Monochoria vaginalis*) and other water weeds will start to grow profusely on the bottom. On the other hand, if the water is too shallow, the ducklings will be mired in mud.

c. The Depth at which Weeds can Germinate

According to "The Ecology and Control of Weeds in Paddy Fields" by Masutsugu Miyahara, the maximum depth below the soil surface at which major weed species can germinate in submerged or water-saturated soil is 2-3 cm for tainubie barnyard millet (*Echinochloa crus-galli Beau. var. oryzicola Ohwi*), 1 cm for duck tongue weed (*Monochoria vaginalis*), 5 mm for smallflower umbrella plant (*Cyperus difformis L.*), and 5 mm for *Rotala indica*. It is surprising how shallow these depths are.

I have observed that the ducks' bills and feet easily reach 2-3 cm under the water. Ducks are thus constantly churning the mud at the depth where weeds can germinate, eating the weed seeds or causing them to float or sink. On the other hand, these weeds are unable to grow from depths that the ducks' bills and feet cannot reach when the paddy field is under water. To achieve good results, it is thus important for the soil in the paddy field to be soft and easy to churn at the early stage when the ducklings are still young.

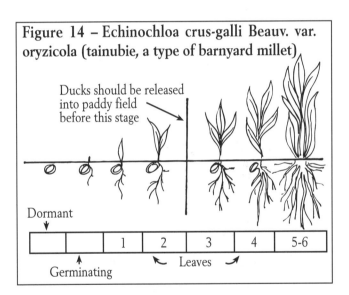

Figure 14 – Echinochloa crus-galli Beauv. var. oryzicola (tainubie, a type of barnyard millet)

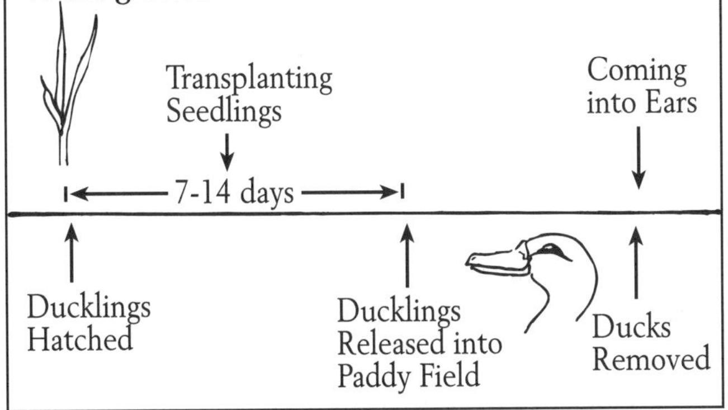

d. The Timing for Releasing the Ducks in Relation to the Growth of the Weeds

A key to weed control is to use deep water to suppress the germination and growth of weeds during the time between transplanting and releasing of the ducklings in the paddy field. Another is to release the ducklings in the paddy field as soon as possible after transplanting the rice seedlings, before the weeds can grow large. These are the two most important points.

As shown in Figure 13, the ducklings that are one or two weeks old should be released in the paddy field as

Figure 13 – Timing for releasing ducks in relation to the growth of weeds

Transplanting Seedlings

Coming into Ears

7-14 days

Ducklings Hatched

Ducklings Released into Paddy Field

Ducks Removed

soon as possible within two weeks of transplanting the rice seedlings. The reason for releasing the ducklings within two weeks is that *Echinochloa crus-galli Beauv. var. oryzicola* (Japanese: tainubie, a type of barnyard millet), the toughest of the weeds that grow in paddy fields, need about two weeks after rice seedling transplantation to grow three leaves. If the ducklings are released before the *Echinochloa crus-galli* grow three leaves, they can be easily controlled as they will be uprooted, float up or get stepped on, and the seeds will be eaten. This is the main reason for releasing the ducks within two weeks of transplantation.

Why is the three leaf stage in the life cycle of the barnyard millet so important? According to my observations, even if the barnyard millet is very thin and weak in the beginning, after the three leaf stage it begins to extend the tips of its leaves out of the water, extend its roots, tiller, and grow sturdy. If it is allowed to grow to this stage, it starts to overtake the rice plants, and the ducks can no longer control it.

Source: Fukuoka Prefecture Crop Research Institute

Weed View "Kusa Miiru"

e. Bird Tillage prior to Transplanting

I have experimented changing the timing for releasing the ducklings in the paddy field, starting 3 weeks after transplanting, then shortening to 2 weeks, 1 week, and 5 days after transplanting, and finally releasing them

Table 6 – Weed Growth as Observed Using Weed Viewer			
	25 June	8 July	10 July
Barnyard millet	1	0	0
duck tongue weed	36	8	2
Rotala indica	over 100	0	0
Lindenia procumbens	1	0	0

Note: Number of weed plants in an area of 50 cm x 50 cm. Investigated by Iizuka Agricultural Extension Center and the Furunos.

on the day of transplanting. Taking this one step further, I tried releasing the ducks in the paddy field before transplanting, and found unexpected benefits. I refer to releasing ducklings into the flooded paddy field prior to transplanting as "Bird Tillage." Bird tillage will prevent the growth of weeds for some time, so that it is not necessary to release the ducklings into the paddy field again for some time after transplantation.

Bird tillage is very effective for controlling weeds when it is not possible to release the ducklings at an early stage for some reason, or in paddy fields that are seeded directly or have many weeds such as barnyard millet.

f. Large Seedlings

In order to effectively control weeds, it is best to increase the depth of the water in the paddy field after transplanting as much as possible (to around 5-10 cm). Thus, it is best to transplant seedlings which are as large and sturdy as possible.

iii. How to Observe the Weeding Mechanism

Why is the mechanism of the weeding effect of ducks still not well understood? Because it is hard to see the weeds growing under the murky water. So what we did was to make a simple frame as shown in the photograph. We called it the "Kusa Miiru" or "Weed Viewer."

If the weed viewer is pressed firmly into the soil of the paddy field and the muddy water is drawn out with a hand operated pump, it is possible to view the newly grown weeds such as barnyard millet and duck tongue weed *(Monochoria vaginalis)* as well as midge larvae and other insects at the bottom. One can see what goes on below the surface ("behind the scenes"), a world to which little attention has been paid in conventional rice farming.

After observation, the weed viewer is removed and two bamboo sticks are planted in the mud to mark the position of the corners of the weed viewer. Two or three days later, the weed viewer is again placed in the same location and the same observations are made. By continuing such observation of the same location, it is possible to understand the weeding mechanism to some extent.

2. Pest Control Effect

i. <u>An epoch-making pest control method using birds as a pest-predator</u>

Integrated Rice and Duck Farming has cleared a path to resolve the problem of weed control, which has been a major obstacle for organic rice farming in Japan. This is true, and has received much publicity.

However, the excellent pest control effect of ducks has received less attention than one might expect. Not so many people seem to take interest in it.

In nature, birds eat many insects and are their main predators. However, hardly any practical research has been done on the use of birds as pest-predators in agriculture, perhaps because birds are able to fly freely over such a wide geographical area.

Conventionally, most research and use of pest-predators in agriculture has focused on spiders and other insects.

Integrated Rice and Duck Farming provides a pest control method that makes the most of the characteristics of waterfowl and the paddy field by enclosing the ducks in the limited space of the paddy field. It has opened a way for use of birds in the paddy field as pest-predators.

ii. <u>Pest Control in Conventional Organic and Low Agrichemical use Rice Farming</u>
   a. Try to grow healthy rice plants by building soil fertility using compost without chemical fertilizers. Avoid adding too much nitrogen to the soil, as this can cause the rice plants to grow too quickly, so that they are not very strong.
   b. Start planting early in March or April to harvest before the season when the brown rice plant hopper (*Nilaparvata lugens*) and other pests grow in large numbers (September - October).
   c. Maintain the natural ecological balance, and promote the growth of spiders and other omnivorous pest-predators.
   d. If unluckily large numbers of plant hoppers appear, pour waste cooking oil or diesel oil on the water surface and shake the rice stalks so that the plant hoppers fall into the oil. (Note: this method is not to be used in integrated rice and duck farming, as it is harmful for the ducks as well as the environment).
   e. Observe the insect pests carefully using a sticky board, and apply insecticide if necessary.

From my limited experience, I feel that it is a bit difficult to control a major outbreak of pests (plant hoppers, etc.) using only pest-predators naturally present in paddy fields. Pest-predators in the paddy field normally live by eating other insects in the paddy field. One would expect there to be a balance between the predators and their prey. The number of spiders would depend upon the amount of food that they could find. It is doubtful whether there would be enough spiders to deal with a large swarm of plant hoppers that suddenly swooped down onto the paddy field.

In a paddy field whose environment has changed suddenly due to submersion under water, will the population of spiders be able to increase quickly enough to deal with the first generation pests such as plant hoppers when they appear?

It has been twenty years since I began organic farming. Before discovering the Integrated Rice and Duck Farming Method, when I was growing rice without using chemicals, weeding by hand, our fields suffered from hopperburn due to brown rice plant hoppers (Nilaparvata lugens) in autumn once every few years. However, I have not experienced this even once in the last ten years since I began Integrated Rice and Duck Farming. The ducks have provided a concrete alternative to spraying pesticides, the most disliked aspect of modern rice farming. This is one thing that makes Integrated Rice and Duck Farming so enjoyable.

iii. The Pest Control Mechanism of Ducks

Note: the mechanism described below has not been fully verified.

The following are thought to be the four reasons for the ducks' pest control effect:

a. The ducks eat the pests
b. The ducks knock the pests into the water with their wings.
c. The ducks chase the pests out of the paddy field.
d. Pests come to dislike the environment of the duck-paddy field.

Rice pests generally live as parasites at the base of the rice stalks and do not move around much, so the ducks can easily eat them. A duckling can catch a small fly in the air while running around. It is born a master bug-catcher.

iv. Weeds are the staple and bugs are the meat

When ducklings are first released in the paddy field, they swim around the paddy field looking very happy.

By and by, they begin to swim in a row while repeatedly stretching their necks out towards the rice leaves. If one watches them with binoculars, one can see that they are apparently eating the insects on the rice leaves. I assume that they make the neck-stretching motion when they are eating insects.

Shortly after being released in the paddy field, the ducks are always in the insect-eating posture. It seems that they mainly eat insects rather than weeds for some time. Probably the weeds are like a staple food such as rice, while the insects are like a delicious meat dish for the ducks.

Insects are a valuable source of protein for the growing ducklings.

v. The Ducks' Style of Pest Control

According to my observations, the duck eats insects in the

Aigamo Duck stretches its neck to eat insects.
(Photo by Lin Xi Quan)

following ways:

a. quickly extending its neck to peck at the leaves above
b. pecking at the base of the rice stalk
c. poking its bill inside the rice stalk
d. eating insects that have fallen on the water surface
e. eating insects that have alighted on grass or enclosure net on the embankment.

Ducks normally move around in a group. They use good teamwork to catch the insects that suddenly fall into the water or fly up.

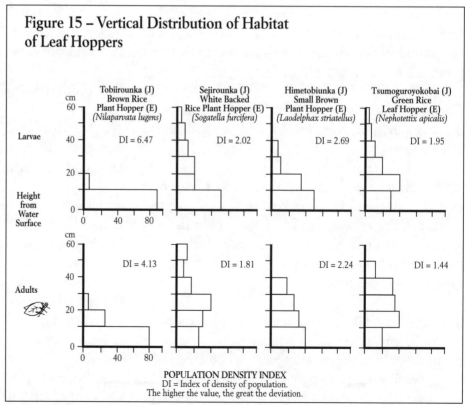

Figure 15 – Vertical Distribution of Habitat of Leaf Hoppers

Tobiirounka (J) Brown Rice Plant Hopper (E) (*Nilaparvata lugens*) — Larvae DI = 6.47, Adults DI = 4.13

Sejirounka (J) White Backed Rice Plant Hopper (E) (*Sogatella furcifera*) — Larvae DI = 2.02, Adults DI = 1.81

Himetobiunka (J) Small Brown Plant Hopper (E) (*Laodelphax striatellus*) — Larvae DI = 2.69, Adults DI = 2.24

Tsumoguroyokobai (J) Green Rice Leaf Hopper (E) (*Nephotettix apicalis*) — Larvae DI = 1.95, Adults DI = 1.44

Height from Water Surface

POPULATION DENSITY INDEX
DI = Index of density of population.
The higher the value, the great the deviation.

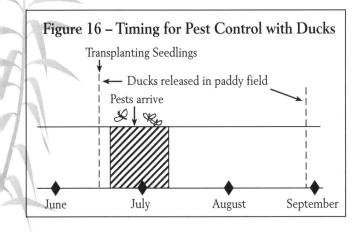

Figure 16 – Timing for Pest Control with Ducks

Transplanting Seedlings
← Ducks released in paddy field
Pests arrive

June · July · August · September

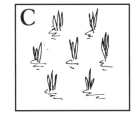

Figure 17 – Overview of Investigated Paddy Field

Duck Plot · Conventional Plot

Table 7 – Degree of Damage in Each Plot

	Duck Plot A	Control Plot B	Conventional Plot C
Number of Tillers	150	124	183
Egg Laying Scars	34	385	671
Scars per Tiller	0.226	3.104	3.666
Proportion	1	13.734	16.221

Table 8 – Total of Insects Found

Duck Plot A	Control Plot B	Conventional Plot C
1	39	80

done, the ducklings will intercept the pests that fly in, catch and eat them, chase them away, and prevent them from laying eggs on the rice stalks. At this stage, the rice plants are still in their early stages of growth and have few leaves, so the ducks can easily find the pests that have alighted on the rice stalks.

If there is a delay in releasing the ducklings into the paddy field, and unluckily the pests lay their eggs, there will be a major outbreak of pest larvae.

Furthermore, at this stage the rice stalks are larger, so it is more difficult for the ducks to find the pests.

vi. Places where the Pests Live

As shown in Figure 15, the brown rice plant hopper *(Nilaparvata lugens)*, which is the worst pest for rice plants in Japan, lives at the base of the rice stalk near the water surface, both at the larval and adult stage. Both the white-backed rice plant hopper *(Sogatella furcifera)* and the small brown plant hopper *(Laodelphax striatellus)* live somewhat higher up on the rice stalk than the brown rice plant hopper, i.e., 10 cm, or at most 20 cm above the water surface. So they are all within reach of the ducks' bills.

On the other hand, the green rice leafhopper *(Nephotettix apicalis)* lives in a wide area ranging from 0 to 40 cm from the water surface. For this reason, the ducks' pest control effect may not be as clear in this case as for plant hoppers. However, ducks can also eat green rice leafhoppers if they stretch their necks.

vii. Timing of Releasing the Ducklings for Pest Control

The method of pest control in Integrated Rice and Duck Farming is very clear and simple. The most important thing is to release an appropriate number of ducklings (15-30 per 10 are, see p33) in the paddy field before the pests fly into the paddy field, or at least before they lay eggs on the rice stalks. If this is

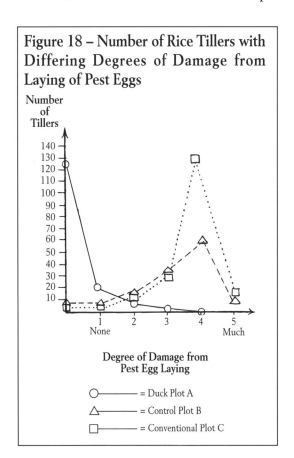

Figure 18 – Number of Rice Tillers with Differing Degrees of Damage from Laying of Pest Eggs

Number of Tillers

Degree of Damage from Pest Egg Laying

○——— = Duck Plot A
△——— = Control Plot B
□——— = Conventional Plot C

Table 9 – Impact of Ducks on Occurrence of Plant Hoppers
(Voluntary Research Group, Fukuoka Prefecture Agricultural Experimentation Station, 1991)
Investigation (15 hills) on 14 July in Keisen-cho. Figures in parenthesis are number per hill

Test Plot	White-backed rice plant hopper adults	White-backed rice plant hopper larvae	Degree of damage from egg laying**	Brown rice plant hopper adults
Duck plot 1	64 (4.3)	5 (0.3)	26.7	0
Duck plot 2	68 (4.5)	6 (0.4)	20.0	0
Duck plot 3	63 (4.7)	8 (0.5)	20.0	0
Control plot	189 (12.6)	136 (9.1)	91.7	1
Conventional plot 1*	61 (4.1)	73 (4.9)	100	1
Conventional plot 2	73 (4.9)	137 (9.1)	100	2

* Conventional plot 1 was sprayed the day before.
** The degree of damage from egg laying = $(4A + 3B + 2C + D)/(4 \times 15)$
A: 91% or more of the stalks had egg laying scars   B: 61-90% of the stalks had egg laying scars
C: 31-60% of the stalks had egg laying scars   D: 1-30% of the stalks had egg laying scars
E: no egg laying scars

Table 10 – Plant Hoppers in a Paddy Field with Aigamo Ducks
(Fifteen hills investigated on 10 August 1991. Figures in parentheses are population per hill.)

Test Plot	White-backed rice plant hoppers		Brown rice plant hopper (J. Tobiirounka)			
	Adult	Larvae	Short Winged Female	Long Winged Female	Male	Larvae
Duck plot 1	7	10	0	0	0	2
Duck plot 2	8	8	0	1	0	0
Duck plot 3	4	14	0	0	0	0
Control plot	50	341	0	2	0	14
	(3.3)	(22.7)	(0)	(0.1)	(0)	(0.9)
Conventional plot	71	46	15	0	10	12
	(1.6)	(1.0)	(0.3)	(0)	(0.2)	(0.3)

*45 hills were examined in the conventional plot
(Voluntary Research Group, Fukuoka Prefecture Agricultural Experimentation Station)

Table 11 – Insects and Disease in Paddy Fields with Aigamo Ducks (19 September 1991)

Plot	Brown rice plant hopper (J. Tobiirounka)		(J. Kabunomeiga) Rice leafroller *Craphalocrosis medinalis*	(J. Mongare byo) Sheath blight *Thanatephorus cucumeris*	(J. Tobimushi) Springtail Collembola	(J. Kymo) Spiders	(J. Aburamushi) Aphids
	Adult	Larvae					
Duck plot 1	1/25 hills	1/25 hills	100/100 hills/hills	37/50 hills/hills	650/20 hills	49/20 hills	14/20 hills
Control plot	3/25	9/25	0	0	231/10	10/10	?
Conventional plot	0	0	35/50	3/50	44/10	17/10	34/10

*Pesticides had been sprayed in paddy fields near the conventional plot
(Investigated by Mr. Noai, Kaho Agricultural Improvement and Extension Center)

Where I live in Kyushu of southern Japan, the pests fly in during late June and early July. In your country, when do rice pests fly in? Please first investigate into this. The secret to defeating pests with ducks is to "make the first move," so that the ducks can intercept the pests as they fly in.

viii. The "Plant Hopper-Interception Effect" of Ducks
Plot A was planted on 13 June with "Hinohikari" rice at a density of 45 hills per 3.3 square meters. 45 Aigamo ducks were released in the paddy field on or after 1 July (10 hatched 17 April, 35 hatched 18 May).

Plot B is a square area of 3 meters by 3 meters enclosed by a 1 meter high fence which prevents the ducks from entering.

Plot C is a conventional paddy field in which chemical fertilizers, pesticides and herbicides are used. Pesticides had not been used prior to the day of the investigation.

Investigator: Mr. Motoyasu Noai, Kaho Agricultural Improvement and Extension Center

Day of Investigation: 11:30 am, 11 July 1991
Method of Investigation: Fifteen randomly chosen rice hills were investigated for damage from laying of pest eggs. The degree of damage was rated on a scale of six. 0-none, 1-slight, 2-some, 3-medium, 4-much, 5-very much damage.

Table 7, with the degree of damage per rice stalk, Table 8, with the total number of insects found, and the graph of Figure 18 clearly show the duck's pest

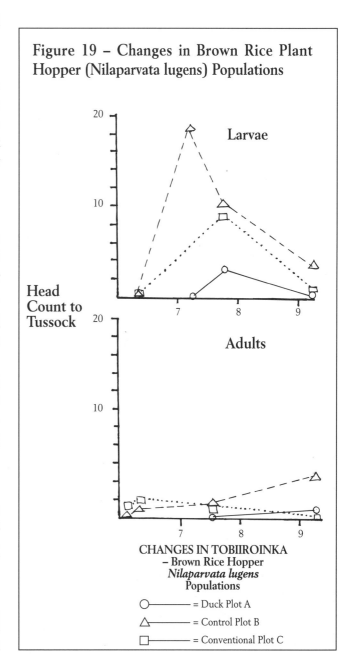

Figure 19 – Changes in Brown Rice Plant Hopper (Nilaparvata lugens) Populations

CHANGES IN TOBIIROINKA
– Brown Rice Hopper
Nilaparvata lugens
Populations

○——— = Duck Plot A
△——— = Control Plot B
□——— = Conventional Plot C

Table 12 – The Types and Amounts of Insects Eaten by Ducks in a Paddy Field

Professor Pu Zhe Long (Zhongshan University, Guangzhou, China), Overview of Pest Control by Raising Ducks, (Dashao Gongse (Sihuixian, Guangdong Province) 19744)

Duck Variety: Hua Zhao   Duck Weight: 400 grams
Tussock height: 57 cm
Water Depth: 3-3.5 cun (1/30 meter) Location: An Er Da Dui   Date: 11 October 1974

Insects Eaten	By 1 duck in 30 min	By 1 duck in 1 hour	By 2 duck in 2 hours
Rice grasshopper	19	25	69
Chinese rice grasshopper	2	4	7
Other rice grasshopper			6
Grasshoppers			3
Mole crickets			1
Green rice leaf hopper	1		12
White-backed rice planthopper		3	3
Young leaf hoppers			16
Adult plant hoppers	1	2	3
Young plant hoppers			18
Young leaf hopper and plant hoppers			36
Cletus trigonus	2	4	12
Scotinophara lurida	3	2	4
Stinkbug	1		3
Stibaropus formosanus	3		5
Parnara guttata adults	1		
Parnara guttata larvae			
Evening brown (Mycalesis gotama) larvae			1
Borers		1	
Whirligig beetles		1	
Small water beetles		7	14
Midges	1	7	
River sheel (viparus)		23	80
Kawanina			52
Other		2	4
Spiders	6	16	50
Carabids		1	2
Ladybug larvae	1		
Flies, heads of leaf hoppers		6	24
Small shrimp			1
TOTAL	**42**	**107**	**427**

Note: Times when ducks were released in the paddy field;
30 min 7:45-8:15, 2 1 hr 7:45-8:45, 2 hr 7:45-9:45. {Average number of insects eaten per duck in 2 hours; 213.5 !}

control effect. Table 7 shows that there was not much difference in the average damage per rice stalk between B and C. From this, it can be inferred that about the same number of plant hoppers and other pests flew into duck paddy field A, control paddy field B and conventional paddy field C.

From Table 8, we can infer that the ducks in duck paddy field A ate or scared away the pests, so that hardly any could lay eggs. The results are shown in Figure 18. Ducks are like sophisticated interceptor missiles.

ix. Ducks Control Pests Well without Killing all the Insects in the Paddy Field

The data of tables 10 and 11 show that the number of pests in the duck plot is much lower than in the control plot or the conventional plot.

The ducks were not able to control rice leaf rollers (*Cnaphalocrecis medinalis*) as effectively as plant hoppers. Perhaps this is because the rice leaf rollers live somewhat higher up on the rice stalk. One clear difference is that the number of beneficial insects such as springtails (Collembola order) and spiders in the duck plot shortly after the ducks were taken out was much higher than the number of beneficial insects in the conventional plot, as shown in Table 11.

The graph in Figure 19 shows that there are much fewer brown rice plant hopper (*Nilaparvata lugens)* larvae and adults in the duck plot than in the control plot. The number is as low as in the conventional plot in which pesticides were used.

x.   The Ducks are Eating the Pests

There are two ways to check the effectiveness of pest control by ducks. One is to compare the numbers and types of pests found on the rice stalks, and the other is to dissect the duck to see what its stomach contains. Refer to Table 12 - conclusions. I have been working with a local agricultural extension worker to catch and dissect the ducks from our paddy field every year. We were surprised to find that one duck had eaten 149 green rice leafhoppers and 856 midge larvae, as shown in Table 13.

xi. Ducks Enrich the Biosphere

Ducks do not annihilate insects in the way that pesticides do. They control their numbers so there is no damage to

Table 13 – Contents of Aigamo Duck Gullet (collected 27 July 1992)
(Survey and Analysis of Integrated Rice and Duck Farming, Research Project of Fukuoka Agricultural Comprehensive Experiment Station, 1992)

Insect	Duck No. 1			Duck No. 2		
	Insect bodies	Dry weight (g)	Percentage of total (%)	Insect bodies	Dry weight (g)	Percentage of total (%)
Midge larvae	856	0.278	9.73	266	0.095	0.64
Green rice leafhopper	149	0.175	6.12	119	0.195	1.31
White-backed rice plant hopper	2	0.001	0.03	0	0	0
Diptera	12	0.037	1.29	4	0.007	0.05
Coleoptera	10	0.021	0.73	25	0.13	0.88
Other insects	0	0	0	3	0.041	0.28
Subtotal insects	**1033**	**0.512**	**17.91**	**417**	**0.468**	**3.16**
Rice grains	73	0.646	22.6	343	5.256	35.44
Bechmannia syzigachne seeds	246	0.282	9.87	193	0.266	1.79
Other seeds	0	0	0	92	0.689	4.65
Duck weed	159	0.027	0.94	0	0	0
Subtotal Plants	**478**	**0.955**	**33.41**	**628**	**6.211**	**41.88**
Unknown	—	1.391	48.67	—	8.15	54.96
TOTAL	**1511**	**2.858**	**99.99**	**1045**	**14.829**	**100**

Notes
1) Duck No. 1 and No. 2 were the same age, but No. 2 was larger.
2) The "gullet" from which the insects were collected is the duck's "crop" or "maw."

the crop. It is typical for a duck paddy field to have more than three times as many spiders as a nearby conventional paddy field. There has been the criticism that "the ecology of the paddy field becomes impoverished when ducks are released, since they eat up all other living things." However, this criticism is self-contradictory. The critic seems to be thinking only about animals such as spiders, insects or Japanese killifish when speaking of the paddy field's ecosystem. Plants are also important constituents of the ecosystem. Growing just one crop, i.e., rice, in the paddy field, in itself seriously impoverishes the ecosystem.

Integrated Rice and Duck Farming is a technique that allows one to utilize the weeds in the paddy field.

Table 14 – Nutrients in Aigamo Duck Manure

(1) Manure Effect of One Duck (2 months in paddy field) (g)

Manure	Nitrogen	Phosphate	Potassium
9,457	47	70	31

(2) Manuring Effect of 20 Ducks per Are (kg)

	Manure	Nitrogen	Phosphate	Potassium
Duck Manure	189	0.94	1.40	0.60
Standard Dosage		6.00	6.00	6.00
Percentage of Standard Dosage		16%	23%	10%

Use of Azolla is a typical example. My duck paddy fields are also teeming with tadpole shrimps, brine shrimps, water fleas, midges (Tokunagayusurika akamusi), diving beetles (*Cybister japonicus*) and other types of insects, as well as Japanese killifish. Even more insects appear where Azolla has been introduced. I think that Integrated Rice and Duck Farming generally enriches the ecosystem of the paddy field. The evaluation of Integrated Rice and Duck Farming changes further if one considers its role as an alternative stockbreeding method.

Table 15 – Nutrients Contained in Feed (Brown Rice Screenings) for Taming Ducks (kg)			
	Nitrogen	Phosphate	Potassium
20kg of brown rice	0.3	0.736	0.532
Fertilizer dosage in conventional paddy	6.5-8.5	7	6.5-7

3. The Nutrient Supplying Effect

i. The Route of Nutrient Supply

For some time after discovering the benefits of ducks, I continued to add compost and fermented organic fertilizers to my paddy fields as in conventional organic rice farming. However, as I watched the ducks swimming freely around the paddy field, I came to think "why bother to wade through the fields to add organic fertilizer?"

In recent years, I have been doing Integrated Rice and Duck Farming without adding any organic fertilizer or compost at any stage in the growing

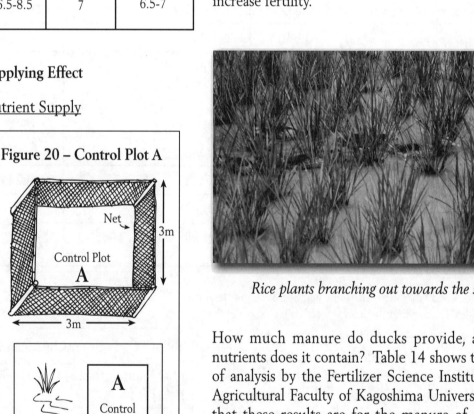

Figure 20 – Control Plot A

Net

3m

Control Plot A

3m

A Control Plot

Duck Plot

cycle, relying only on the ducks and the natural fertility of the paddy field. Nonetheless, the soil fertility has continued to improve, and harvests have been good year after year. In fall of 1996, we harvested 807kg paddy rice, 647 kg (brown rice) = per 10 a without use of any fertilizers (Iizuka Agricultural Extension Center). Of course, this does not mean that rice will grow well without fertilizer in any paddy field even if its soil is infertile. Still, it is a fact that I could get harvests of more than 750kg paddy rice, 600 kg (=)/10 a without using any fertilizer. Why was this possible?

Since there is no major difference in the composition of the harvested rice, the necessary nutrients must have been supplied somehow. There are two main ways in which the ducks' nutrient supplying effect is achieved. One is that the ducks manure the fields. The other is that the activity of the ducks promotes decomposition of organic matter in the soil, supplying nutrients that increase fertility.

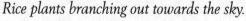

Rice plants branching out towards the sky.

How much manure do ducks provide, and what nutrients does it contain? Table 14 shows the results of analysis by the Fertilizer Science Institute of the Agricultural Faculty of Kagoshima University. Note that these results are for the manure of cage-bred Aigamo ducks, not ducks in a paddy field.

According to this, the amount of manure provided by 20 Aigamo ducks in an area of 10 a in two months would be 189 kilograms. This would provide 940 grams of nitrogen, 1400 grams of phosphate and 600 grams of potassium to the soil. This is only 10-20% of the amount of fertilizer that would normally be added in a conventional paddy field.

During the two months when I raise them in the paddy field, I feed the ducks 20 kg of rice screenings per 10 a. This is the only external input to the duck paddy field. The amount of nitrogen, phosphate and potassium contained in 20 kg of brown rice is as shown in Table 15. Even twice this amount would be very little, as with the duck manure.

4. The Full-Time Ploughing and Muddying Effect ("F Effect")

i. Let's Make a Control Plot

Ever since 1991, when I at last won the bitter battle against dogs, I have been making a control plot in my paddy field, as shown in Figure 20. The control plot is an area of 3 m x 3 m enclosed by a 1 meter high net to prevent the entry of ducks. Being an ordinary farmer, it was very useful for me to make a control plot, since I could directly observe and compare the growth of weeds, pests, and the rice plants over time with my own eyes.

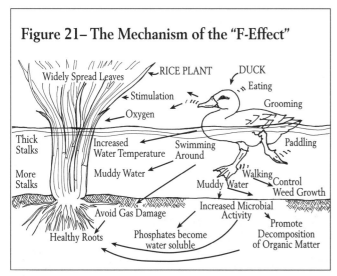

Figure 21– The Mechanism of the "F-Effect"

Following my intuition, I asked the researchers from the local agricultural extension center, agricultural experiment station, and university to investigate the duck plot and control plot every year. This research data helped me to recognize the significance of "direct perception" and to think about and combine various techniques.

The control plot elucidates the effect of ducks in the paddy field. I encourage you to make a control plot if you practise Integrated Rice and Duck Farming.

ii. The Shape of the Rice Plant

Every year, a clear difference has been observed between the shape of the rice plants in the control plot and that of the rice plants in the duck plot. The rice plants in the duck plot are found to have more stems than those in the control plot; the stems are thicker, and spread out towards the sky like the water of a fountain. The stalks are stout, and the underground roots are also extremely well developed. The rice plants are very sturdy overall.

iii. What is the "F-Effect"?

There is an old saying in Japan that "you'll get a good rice harvest if the water in the paddy field is muddy." When ducks are released in the paddy field, their activity soon makes the water muddy. The water can also become muddy in a conventional paddy field, but only when people enter the plot to weed or do other work. The water becomes clear again shortly after people get out of the field. However, the water in the duck paddy field is muddy for the entire two months that the ducks are kept there. This phenomenon is probably unique to Integrated Rice and Duck Farming. I refer to the effect of the physical activity of the ducks using their feet and bills and the effect of the resulting muddy water as the "full-time ploughing and muddying effect."

iv. The Mechanism of the Full-time Ploughing and Muddying Effect

In a duck paddy field, the water level is kept high and the ducks stir up the mud using their feet and bills. For this reason, the oxygen dissolved in the water is not readily absorbed by the soil, and the oxygen in the soil is released into the water. Furthermore, due to the ducks' nutrient supplying effect, microorganisms increase in number and consume the oxygen, causing

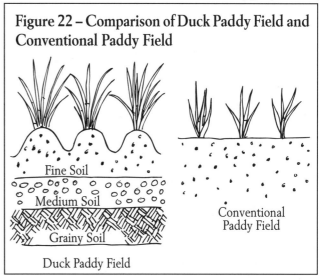

Figure 22 – Comparison of Duck Paddy Field and Conventional Paddy Field

Fine Soil

Medium Soil

Grainy Soil

Duck Paddy Field

Conventional Paddy Field

reduction (deoxidation). Reduction causes insoluble phosphates (e.g., iron phosphate) to become water soluble, so that the rice plants can absorb them and become stronger. Reduction also prevents ammonium from becoming nitrified, thus preventing loss of nitrogen due to runoff.

v. <u>Interesting Aspects of the Muddy Water Effect</u>
As mentioned above, the clear difference in the shape of the rice plants between the duck plot and the control plot cannot be said to result just from having muddy water in the paddy field for two months. The control plot was in the same paddy field as the duck plot, so the water conditions were the same. The muddy water containing duck manure was passing through the net into the control plot, so both the duck plot and the control plot had muddy water. Then what was the reason for the unmistakable difference in the shape of the rice plants?

As shown in the photograph (p.31), I put dirt in two plastic containers, filled them with water, planted rice seedlings, and installed a water pump to create muddy water in one of the containers. On comparison, it was found that there was much less growth of weeds in the muddy water than in the clear water. However, there was no obvious difference in the growth of the rice plants such as observed between the duck plot and the control plot. The improved tillering and branching out of the rice plant is not a result of the muddy water, but is thought to be due to the physical action of the duck rubbing against the rice plant's roots and stalks and removing the mud at the base of the stalks with its bill, feet, etc.

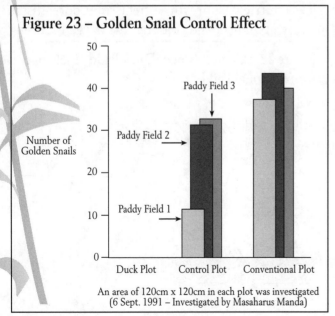

Figure 23 – Golden Snail Control Effect

Number of Golden Snails

Paddy Field 3

Paddy Field 2

Paddy Field 1

50
40
30
20
10
0

Duck Plot   Control Plot   Conventional Plot

An area of 120cm x 120cm in each plot was investigated
(6 Sept. 1991 – Investigated by Masaharus Manda)

vi. <u>The F-Effect Transforms the Paddy Field</u>
a. Muddy Water Makes the Soil Feel Like Pudding

The soil of a paddy field in which ducks have been released feels very soft and silky like pudding. In contrast, the soil of the control plot and the conventional plot, in which ducks are not kept, feels gritty. There is an unmistakable difference in how they feel to the touch. This is a phenomenon occurring not only in our paddy fields, but throughout Japan and various Asian countries where Integrated Rice and Duck Farming is being practiced. It is a result of the full-time ploughing and muddying effect.

If the soil is sliced and examined after the water is drained from the duck paddy field, one finds that the top 5 cm of soil has a three layered structure. At the top there is a clay layer with very fine particles. Next is a layer with somewhat larger soil particles, and below that is a sandy layer with grainy soil. Interestingly, the soil of the control plot and the conventional plot did not have such a distinct layered structure.

When the F-Effect creates this three layer soil structure, the paddy field is able to hold water very well when under water. The fine clay on the surface is thought to prevent leakage of water when the paddy field is under water.

Duck controlling golden snails in the Philippines.

This has been especially good news for terraced paddy fields in the mountains. One farmer said to me, "Mr. Furuno, I have terraced paddy fields in the mountains, and used to have a problem with water leakage. I used to plaster the walls of my paddy field with mud, and had a hard time keeping the water in. But the water retention has improved greatly since I started keeping ducks in the paddy field. It really helps!" This should also be the case in rice terraces in mountainous areas throughout Asia.

On the other hand, when harvest approaches and it is time to drain the water, the three-layered soil of the duck paddy field dries very easily. Due to the three-layered structure of the soil, the surface clay shrinks after the water is drained, forming large cracks that promote the vertical percolation of the water.

Furthermore, shallow grooves are formed in the soil between the rows of rice plants, due to the ducks' frequent passing back and forth between the rows. These grooves help the surface water to run off quickly. Thus, duck paddy fields dry well after being drained.

5. The Golden Snail Control Effect

Fortunately, so far there are no golden snails in my village. I don't know so much about the relationship between ducks and golden snails. However, I have observed that ducks love to eat mollusks. The ducklings began to eat small shellfish immediately after being released.

I have heard that Aigamo ducklings that have just been released in the paddy field avidly eat newly born golden snails. It is said that the ducks eat larger golden snails as they become larger, so that there are no large golden snails in the paddy field in autumn.

However, I am told that there can be damage from golden snails early in the season when the ducklings are still small, since the large golden snails that damage the rice plants are too big for the ducks to eat. Damage can be prevented the next year as long as the golden snails do not creep in from elsewhere.

In Bukidonon in Mindanao, the Philippines, which I visited in the Spring of 1997, farmers were releasing many large ducks into the paddy fields one month before transplanting, in order to get rid of golden snails.

Golden snails are a very valuable source of protein for ducks, and can be used to raise them. The unsavory meat of the golden snails can be converted to delicious duck meat.

Ducks are experts at getting rid of golden snails. They exhibit tremendous power, whether released in waterways or in the paddy fields. We should try to make the most of the remarkable capabilities of ducks.

6. Stimulation of the Rice Plants

I have observed that rice plants in duck paddy fields tend to have more and thicker stalks, to be sturdier, and to branch out more than rice plants in paddy fields without ducks. This tendency is generally more noticeable the wider the spacing is between the rice plants, the more ducks are kept, and the earlier they are released in the paddy field. Why is the shape of the rice plant affected in this way? It seems that the plant hormone ethylene is involved.

The ducks are constantly stimulating the rice plants, touching them as they move around in a group. Not only are they always stimulating the base of the rice stalks by poking them with their bills, as mentioned above. They are also rubbing against the rice plants with their whole body. They strike the rice leaves as they flap their wings while swimming, eat the insects on the leaves, and poke their heads inside the rice stalks, stimulating the entire plant above the ground. At the same time, they also physically stimulate the roots underground. I hypothesize that the stimulus from contact by ducks promotes formation of ethylene in the plants, causing them to take on their unique shape.

The rice stimulation effect.

Chapter Two

The Practice of Integrated Rice and Duck Farming in Japan

The natural, social and economic conditions of your country are probably totally different from those of Japan. Thus, it may not be possible to apply the method of Integrated Rice and Duck Farming used in Japan in your country without adaptation.

Next, I will be writing about the current situation in Japan. I hope that this will provide a basis for you to develop your own method of Integrated Rice and Duck Farming suited to the conditions of your country.

I. How Many Ducks are Appropriate?

The number of ducks used in Integrated Rice and Duck Farming is decided based on comprehensive analysis of the six main effects of the ducks: the weed control effect, the pest control effect, the nutrient supplying effect, the full-time ploughing and muddying effect, the rice plant stimulation effect and the golden snail control effect. As a rule, I decide the number of ducks on the basis of the amount of weeds, insects and other natural duck feed available in a 10 a area, and how many are required so that the ducks are always active throughout the entire paddy field.

According to my experience, the appropriate number of Aigamo ducks to be released in the paddy field is 15 to 30 per 10 a.

For instance, in an area where weeds do not grow much, it may be possible to get adequate weed control with 10 or fewer ducks. However, would 10 or less ducks be enough to control pests and supply nutrients? Of course, the optimum number depends upon the dynamic balance between the rice plants, weeds, insects and ducks, so it is not fixed.

For instance, I had taught the farmers in Haiphong in northern Vietnam that they should keep 15-30 ducks per 10 a. However, they have been keeping 45 - 60 ducks per 10 a, about 3 times the appropriate number in Japan, and have been having good results. I think this is fine. It is also quite interesting from the standpoint of stockbreeding.

II. Area and Method of Paddy Field Enclosure

Since it is ducks rather than people that do the work in Integrated Rice and Duck Farming, the area of cultivation can be expanded without limit. There are some farming households in Japan that are doing Integrated Rice and Duck Farming in an area of nearly 10 hectares. However, I think it is a bit reckless to try to enclose 2 or 3 hectares at once from the start.

Then, what is the maximum area of paddy field that can be enclosed? The largest enclosure I ever made was 60 a with about 120 ducks. It went ok for the most part. According to my experience, the likelihood of damage to the rice seedlings in the beginning increases if more than 100 ducks are kept together. The results should be ok if no more than 100 ducks are kept in an area of no more than 30 are.

At first, it is probably best to experiment with a paddy field of less than 30 are :

1. **When two 30 are paddy fields are adjacent to each other, the levee separating the two plots should be divided to provide resting places for the ducks, as shown in Figure 24.**

Figure 24 – When two 30 a plots are adjacent to each other

Figure 25 – When a number of paddy fields (total area less than 30 a) are grouped together

2. When many Paddy Fields are grouped together

When a number of small paddy fields lay next to each other and their total area is less than 30 a, it should be ok to surround them all with one enclosure.

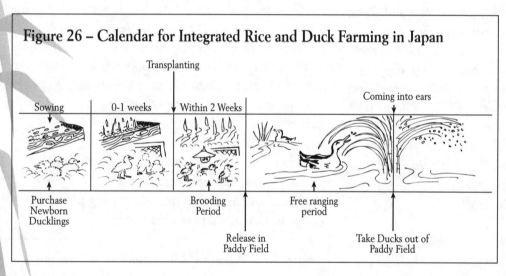

Figure 26 – Calendar for Integrated Rice and Duck Farming in Japan

Transplanting

Sowing | 0-1 weeks | Within 2 Weeks | | Coming into ears

Purchase Newborn Ducklings | | Brooding Period | Free ranging period | Take Ducks out of Paddy Field

Release in Paddy Field

III. From when and how long should the ducks be kept in the Paddy Field?

As shown in Figure 26, in Japan, ducklings which are 1-2 weeks old are usually released in the paddy field within two weeks of transplanting, at a density of 15-30 per 10 a. The timing for releasing the ducks varies greatly depending on the timing for transplanting rice seedlings, the temperature, and the rice cultivation method of each country.

IV. Breeding

Appropriate Breeds (Local Ducks are Best)
The following varieties of ducks are used for Integrated Rice and Duck Farming in Japan:

1. Aigamo duck - a cross between a domesticated female and wild male duck, rather small with tasty meat (1.5 kg)
2. Aokubi (green necked) duck - a somewhat larger duck with similar appearance to Aigamo duck (2.3-2.4 kg)
3. Cherry Valley duck - a large duck native to England (more than 3.5 kg)
4. Ma duck - native to China (more than 2 kg)

There are a number of varieties, but the Aigamo duck is used the most. Local varieties of ducks that can be seen playing in ponds or paddy fields should be best for Integrated Rice and Duck Farming in your country.

V. How to Raise the Ducklings

One can hardly see any ducks in the rural areas of Japan nowadays. Normally, in other Asian countries, one meets ducks everywhere. I feel a bit shy to try to explain duck raising to the readers in other Asian countries, where duck raising is just a part of everyday life, but I will try anyway. The reason is that Integrated Rice and Duck Farming requires a somewhat different perspective than duck raising as stockbreeding.

1. Ducklings Are Seven Tenths of the Crop

In Japan there is the saying "the seedlings are half of the crop." Likewise, in Integrated Rice and Duck Farming, once you have had good results raising the ducklings, you have practically succeeded! In fact, the ducklings later on play such an important role in the growth of the rice plants that it could be said that "ducklings are seven tenths of the crop." Regardless, our objective is to raise healthy, sturdy bodied ducklings.

2. How to Build the Brooder and Maintain the Right Temperature

A brooder such as I explain below is probably unnecessary in warm countries of Southeast Asia, Africa, etc., but it is required in temperate Japan to maintain a proper temperature and protect the ducklings from predators.

I have been building brooders with my own hands. They are made of cedar planks, which are lightly nailed together at the corners. When not in use, they can be taken apart and stored as four planks.

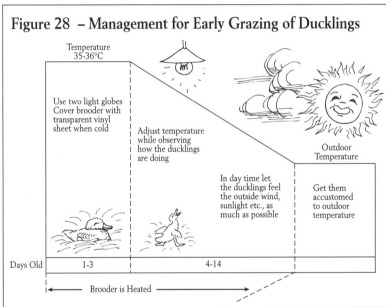

Figure 28 – Management for Early Grazing of Ducklings

Temperature 35-36°C

Use two light globes Cover brooder with transparent vinyl sheet when cold

Adjust temperature while observing how the ducklings are doing

In day time let the ducklings feel the outside wind, sunlight etc., as much as possible

Get them accustomed to outdoor temperature

Outdoor Temperature

Days Old   1-3   4-14

Brooder is Heated

To maintain a constant temperature, I lay a Styrofoam slab on the floor, and cover it with about 20 cm of rice husks. I use a light bulb (such as used in poultry sheds) to prevent it from getting cold inside. The brooder is covered with wire mesh to keep out predators.

3. Temperature Management

Figure 28 gives an example of the method of brooder temperature management that I have used so that the ducklings can be released in the paddy field as soon as possible (at an age of 2-3 weeks). The method would vary considerably depending on the country and time of the year.

VI. Daily Care of the Ducklings

1. Feeding

Since ducks are waterfowl, they have a habit of alternately eating feed and drinking water. They seem to have difficulty eating without water. Please make sure to give them feed and water at the same time.

For three days after the Aigamo ducklings arrive, I feed them rice screenings. After that, I give them chicken feed that I compound myself. Feeding is twice a day. Just enough feed should be given so that some feed is left after two hours, but all is eaten up before it is time to feed them again.

It is not good for there to always be feed in the feeder. Continuous feeding will make the ducklings too plump too soon, causing problems. If the ducklings are too big, they will sometimes step on and knock over the rice seedlings or eat the rice leaves when released in the paddy field.

Raising plump ducklings by continuous feeding may be good for stockbreeding, but it is taboo in Integrated Rice and Duck Farming. This is because our objective is to release the ducklings in the paddy field, not merely to fatten them.

2. Give Plenty of Green Feed

Plenty of green feed should be given to the ducklings so they will be ready to eat the weeds in the paddy field. Green feed is rich in vitamins and minerals, and helps the duck to develop its digestive system.

3. Water Supply

Since ducks are waterfowl, they have a habit of indiscriminately jumping into water from the time they are small ducklings. For this reason, it is essential to use a water tray that is only wide enough for the ducklings to stick their bills in. If the water tray is wide enough to fit the duckling's body, the ducklings will jump into the water and get sopping wet. They may die, unable to adjust to the temperature change. The key to water supply is to make sure that there is always water in the water tray, but that the whole floor of the brooder does not get wet.

4. Water Training

When should one begin the ducklings' water training? In the beginning, I was worried that my dear ducklings would get wet and die, so I only started water training when they were about three weeks old.

However, I learned that, in early summer, wild ducklings will jump into the water as soon as they are hatched, and crawl under the parent duck's wings if they become cold. If the parent duck has several eggs, it is normal for the first-hatched ducklings to be jumping into the water while the parent is still sitting on the other eggs. I am told that the ducklings hop into the water as soon as they are hatched.

Bathing must be instinctual behavior of waterfowl. I let the ducklings bathe for a few minutes shortly after they are hatched. I increase the duration and frequency of bathing each day, and build a bathing pond and exercise area next to the brooder after a few days.

It seems that letting the ducklings bathe from the time they are hatched helps them to naturally learn to oil their feathers and adjust their body temperature.

Bathing and the right amount of exercise promote the growth of the waterfowl's muscles, bones and feathers, and are basic to raising healthy ducklings. Ducklings which have been overfed and haven't gotten enough exercise are unsuitable for Integrated Rice and Duck Farming.

Ducks playing in the water.

In brief, it is essential to give the ducklings rigorous water training from the very beginning, so that they learn to oil their feathers and adjust to the water and temperature change, if you want to release them into the paddy field when they are two weeks old.

Water training is particularly important in Japan, since it is still rather cold when the rice seedlings are transplanted. Perhaps it is not so necessary in the tropics of Southeast Asia or other regions.

VII. The Actual Method of Releasing Ducks in the Paddy Field

1. Timing and Conditions for Releasing in the Paddy Field

The following four conditions must be met in order to release ducks into the paddy field for the first time:

i. To the extent possible, get rid of any wild dogs, weasels, foxes or other predators in the area.
ii. Finish setting up the electric fence or net around the paddy field.
iii. Make sure that the rice seedlings are sturdy and stable enough so that they do not get knocked own or crushed by the ducks' swimming around.
iv. Make sure that the ducklings are strong and accustomed to water, so that they can adapt to temperature change when in the water.

2. The Rice and Ducks are Classmates

When I release Aigamo ducklings in my paddy field, they are 7 to 14 days old. I release 20-30 ducklings per 10 a. This is just about the right proportion for releasing the ducklings early without damaging the rice plants.

If there are many barnyard millet plants and weeds in the paddy field, about 5 middle-size ducks (4 weeks old) are mingled with the 20-30 ducklings. When this is done, the whole paddy field becomes quite muddy from the first day, maximizing the duck effect. It is also effective to add just one middle-size duck to the flock. It will play the role of leader (mother), warning the ducklings of any approaching predators or guiding them to resting places.

The ducklings are released within two weeks of transplanting the rice seedlings. The seedlings that I transplant are 40 days old with an average of 5.3 leaves. I transplant seedlings which are as sturdy as possible, and introduce small ducklings, so that the seedlings are not damaged. The rice plants and the ducklings are classmates, growing big together. Maintaining a balance between them is important.

Aigamo duckling and rice seedlings.

3. From when and how long to Release the Ducks in the Paddy Field

As a rule, the ducklings are released in the paddy field within two weeks of transplantation of rice seedlings. After that, they are kept in the paddy field day and night. The ducks are removed from the paddy field when the rice plants come into ears.

When the rice plants begin to sag under the weight of the ears, the ducks will jump up to eat the rice ears. Once they begin to eat the ears of rice, the ducks will not readily gather around you even if you give them feed. You will have a hard time catching them.

To summarize, in Japan, the ducks are kept in the paddy field for the two months from transplanting till the rice plants come into ears.

4. Water Training in the Paddy Field

The objectives of giving the ducks water training in the paddy field are:

i. To get them accustomed to adjusting their body temperature and moving around together in the paddy field.

ii. To get them to remember their shed for avoiding rain and sleeping at night.

Firstly, an area of about 5 m x 5 m including the resting shed is enclosed with a net or plastic sheets (corrugated sheets used to reinforce levees), as shown in Figure 29. Fishing line is extended over the top at 2 meter intervals to keep out crows.

Of course, in Japan, the paddy field is surrounded with an electric fence.

Once the above preparations have been made, the Aigamo ducklings are gently placed in the dry land area on a windless morning. The ducklings will jump right into the water, but they will soon come back up on the dry land to dry their feathers, as the enclosed area is not very large. One must make sure to give them feed at this time.

If one releases the ducklings into the large paddy field from the very beginning, there are cases that they will not know that they can rest in the shed. They may panic in a sudden rainfall, not knowing where to take shelter. It is important that the ducklings learn to go to the shed to dry their feathers, rest at night, and take shelter from the rain. Perhaps this would be unnecessary in your paddy fields in warm countries of the south - what do you think?

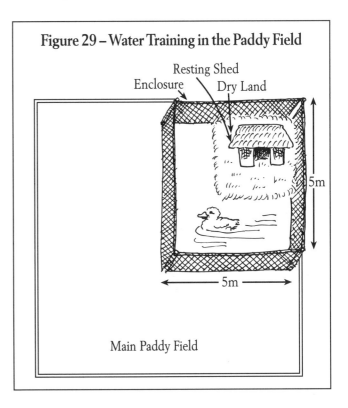

Figure 29 – Water Training in the Paddy Field

5. Feeding the Ducks in the Paddy Field

From my observations, I sense that ducks tend to just get fat and sit on the levees if they are given too much feed. They cannot do good work if they are full. The objective of giving feed to the Aigamo ducks released in the paddy field is not just to fatten them, as in the case of regular stockbreeding. The objective is use feeding as a medium of communication with the ducks.

I feed the ducks in my paddy twice everyday, at a regular time in the morning and the evening. At this time, I communicate with the ducks and observe them and the rice plants closely.

First, I go to the paddy field in the morning and call to the ducks: "koi! koi!" (come here!). They usually come hurrying to me right away. Once they have come, I give them feed while counting to see roughly how many there are.

If the ducks don't come immediately, it means something went wrong during the previous night. For instance, they may have been threatened or attacked by a predator.

I also feed the ducks in the evening. At this time, I mainly check carefully to see that the net or electric fence is not damaged.

Of course, I also carefully check the growth of the rice plants, the occurrence of weeds, pests or diseases, any damage due to the ducks' activity, etc., every morning and evening.

Looking at the paddy field and comparing it to the control plot (mentioned above) day by day is one of the great pleasures of farming.

The feed is not cast into the water, but is given to the ducks on a sheet or cloth placed on the ground. If weeds start to grow vigorously in one part (S) of the paddy field because the ground is somewhat higher (the water is shallower) there, the feed should be cast into that area (S) for 2-3 days. The ducks will voraciously eat the feed, and they will also eat the weeds and step on them. The weeds in that area (S) will eventually disappear. However, there are cases that the ducks damage the rice plants because of too much activity in that one area, so one needs to observe carefully and respond appropriately. This is one way of using feed to achieve an even "duck effect" throughout the paddy field.

6. When Ducks Damage the Rice Plants

There are a number of factors that determine whether the ducks cause damage to the rice plants after they are released into the paddy field, such as:
i.   the size of the rice seedlings
ii. the size of the ducklings
iii. the amount of weeds, insects, and feed given
iv. how well the rice plant is growing

The situation varies depending on the balance between the ducks and the rice plants. I will give some examples for your reference.

When the Seedlings are too Weak
Once my rice was damaged because I let the ducks swim around in a place where the rice seedings were too weak, with soft leaves which were floating on the water surface. The rice seedlings sank into the mud and died.

When the Ducks are too Big
Even if the rice seedlings are fairly sturdy, there are cases that they get stepped on and sink into the mud if, due to a delay, the ducklings are too big when released in the paddy field. It seems that the over-sized ducklings will also sometimes eat the leaves of the rice seedlings that have gotten soft after being pushed into the mud.

When there are not enough Weeds in the Paddy Field
If rather large ducklings are released into a paddy field that does not have much naturally available food, there are cases that they will eat the tips of the rice leaves. Once they develop such a habit, it is hard to stop it. In such cases, it is best to take the ducklings out of that paddy field and release them in a different paddy field, or to keep them in a shed for some time before releasing them in the paddy field again.

A Pond is Formed In Part of the Paddy Field
There are cases that a part of the paddy field in which ducks have been released loses its rice seedlings, becoming like a pond. This occurs in the following cases:

i. At an early stage, the rice seedlings get damaged in an area where the ducks pass frequently near their feeding or resting place, so that the area becomes like a pond.

ii. The seedlings get submerged and then die as a result of the ducks' muddying effect in places where the water is deep, such as near the water inlet or where the ground is uneven.

iii. The rice plants in the middle of the paddy field are stepped on and eaten by the ducks, who have huddled together in a circle, facing outwards, all night long, for fear of dogs, foxes, or other predators that have been lurking around the paddy field.

I call such phenomena "Aigamo Mystery Circles." Prevention measures include keeping a balance in the size of the rice seedlings and ducks, making sure that the paddy field is level, and keeping predators away.

VIII. Predator Control

1. Duck Predators in Japan

The predators that attack ducks released in paddy fields in Japan are dogs, weasels, foxes, raccoon dogs, cats, and crows, which attack from the sky. In Integrated Rice and Duck Farming, ducks are kept in the paddy field day and night for approximately two months, so protecting them from predators is very important.

Many people in Japan worry about predators, saying "our paddy fields are too far from our house, so we can't keep ducks in them." However, whether the paddy field is 1 kilometer away or just 100 meters away from home, once the curtain of evening descends, the paddy field is totally dark. Distance makes no difference.

Dogs, weasels, foxes, raccoon dogs, and cats will attack the ducks regardless of their size, but normally crows primarily attack small ducklings. What sort of duck predators are there in your country?

2. The Basics of Predator Control

The lessons I have learned from my long relationship with ducks are "make the first move," "be creative," and "be tenacious."

i. Make the First Move

The secret to winning the battle against predators is to make the first move. If the predators succeed even once to invade the paddy field and taste the delicious duck meat, they will continue to try desperately to get in, no matter how carefully you guard the ducks. The lesson I learned from the predators after many bitter experiences is that the period immediately after releasing the ducks in the paddy field each year is crucial. One must take the utmost precaution to make sure that the ducklings are not attacked at this time. The first two weeks are the key.

ii. Be Creative

Predators never become "used to" an electric fence or other measure that gives a direct physical stimulus. However, methods to merely scare the predator, such as hanging up a dead crow or dog, lose effectiveness over time, as the predators get accustomed to them. So new methods have to be thought up. It is like a cat-and-mouse game. It is important to closely observe the behavior of the predators with one's own eyes, and to keep thinking up new ideas. Use intelligence to defeat the predators.

iii. Be Tenacious

Combat with predators is an exhausting battle of nerves. In the beginning, I used to stay up all night keeping guard against predators. The moment my attention lapsed, the moment I muttered "enough!" out of sheer exhaustion, the predators would attack. It was as if they could read my mind. One needs tenacity not to lose to the predators. It is a test of will power.

3. The Behavior of Duck Predators in Japan

i. Dogs

In Japan, both wild dogs and domesticated dogs attack ducks. I have many times seen a normally very docile dog suddenly turn "wild" and try to attack ducks. Dogs normally attack ducks at night. However, they will also attack in morning or daytime if no one is around.

Worst of all, dogs don't attack ducks just to eat them. They kill them one after another for "sport." It is not uncommon for a dog to kill a hundred ducks in one night if it gets into the paddy field. As far as I have heard, it seems to be quite rare for dogs to attack ducks in China, Indonesia, Vietnam, or other countries where ducks are ubiquitous.

ii. Foxes and Raccoon Dogs

In Japan, both foxes and raccoon dogs are extremely clever natural predators of ducks. They are good at tearing nets or nimbly climbing up them. They can be difficult to keep out no matter how high or strong the net is. However, they differ from dogs in that they kill to eat, and carry off their prey with them.

iii. Weasels

Weasels are also important duck predators. What makes them tough adversaries is that they can break in through even the smallest of spaces to attack the ducks. Typically, weasels bite small holes in the ducks' necks and suck their blood.

iv. Crows

Crows are also among the main predators of ducks. They normally attack ducklings when they are small, unaccustomed to the water, and haven't learned to move in groups. However, crows are territorial, so there are only three crows that attack the ducks in our paddy fields.

4. Predator Control in Practice

The First Line of Defense is Water

Water is basic to predator control in the paddy field. Ducks waddle around quite slowly on dry land, but can swim around very swiftly in the water of the paddy field. Whenever an enemy approaches, they immediately escape into water.

Unfortunately, the water in the paddy fields is only about 10 cm deep, so it is not possible to keep predators out just with water as in a pond. Still, the water in the paddy field is important for protecting the ducks from predators. If one tries draining the water from the paddy field, one finds that the ducks become more vulnerable to attacks by predators.

Countermeasures against Dogs, Foxes, Raccoon Dogs and Weasels

i. Box Traps

In Japan, it is important to get rid of wild dogs using box traps before releasing the ducks into the paddy field.

ii. Steel Traps

Steel traps are also effective. Weasels, which like to crawl in through small holes, can be captured before the ducks are released in the paddy field, by opening a small hole in a cardboard box and placing a raw egg and a steel trap inside, as shown in Figure 31. In Japan, weasels love raw eggs. For the first 2-3 days, only a raw egg is put in the box. Eventually, the egg will have disappeared by the morning. Seeing that it has been taken, one places the steel trap next to the egg on the third day. The weasel can be caught for certain this way.

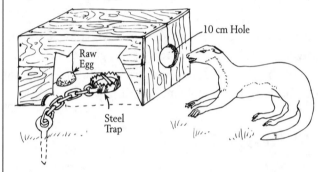

Figure 31 – How to Catch Weasels with a Steel Trap and Raw Eggs

iii. Nets

In Japan, it is common to place a 1.2 - 1.5 meter high net around the duck paddy field as shown in Figure 32, to keep out dogs, foxes, raccoon dogs and other predators. A small rope is looped through the bottom edge of the net, which is firmly embedded into the mud. The main point is to make sure that the bottom of the net is firmly fixed in the ground. In areas with few predators, there are cases that such a simple net can keep the ducks from getting out and prevent the intrusion of predators. For the first three years, I tried to keep out predators using such a simple net.

However, in Japan, where dogs are very common, large dogs will easily jump over a 1.5 meter net. No matter how strong or high the net is, they can get in by digging under the net.

However, in Vietnam and other Asian countries with a long history of raising ducks, it is generally rare for dogs to attack ducks, so farmers have succeeded in keeping out predators with a simple net of only about 50 cm height. It is interesting that the relationship between dogs and ducks varies so much from country to country.

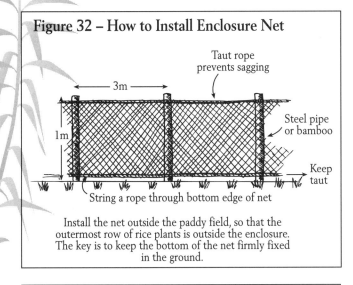

Figure 32 – How to Install Enclosure Net

Taut rope prevents sagging

3m

1m

Steel pipe or bamboo

Keep taut

String a rope through bottom edge of net

Install the net outside the paddy field, so that the outermost row of rice plants is outside the enclosure. The key is to keep the bottom of the net firmly fixed in the ground.

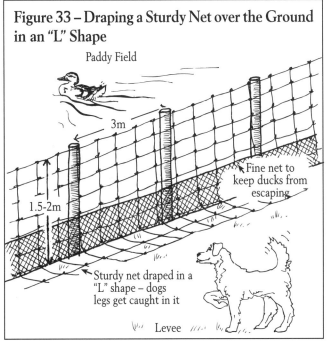

Figure 33 – Draping a Sturdy Net over the Ground in an "L" Shape

Paddy Field

3m

1.5-2m

Fine net to keep ducks from escaping

Sturdy net draped in a "L" shape – dogs legs get caught in it

Levee

At one time, I used to keep predators out by placing a 2 meter high sturdy, loose-mesh net on the inside of the levee, and draping the bottom of the net over the levee in an "L" shape, as shown in Figure 33. The dogs feet get tangled in the part of the net draped over the ground, making it hard for them to get in. This method is a bit troublesome, but is effective for keeping dogs out. However, the net has to be firmly fixed to strong stakes, or the net will fall down while the dog is struggling with its legs tangled in the net. The main point is that the net should be draped loosely over the ground, rather than be taut.

iv. Electric Fence

For three years, I tried to keep out predators just using nets. However, I failed each time, and the dogs continued to attack the ducks. After many failures, I at last arrived at the idea of using an electric fence. I emerged victorious in the battle with dogs. This led to the rapid spread of Integrated Rice and Duck Farming throughout Japan.

The Physical Fence and The Psychological Fence

There are two types of fences, physical ones and psychological ones. A physical fence is one (such as the nets mentioned above) that physically prevents the intrusion of animals. A psychological fence is one that has a psychological effect on the predator such that it prefers not to come in, even if it could.

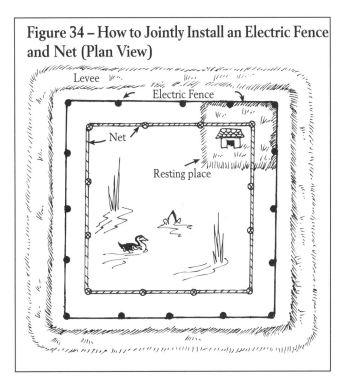

Figure 34 – How to Jointly Install an Electric Fence and Net (Plan View)

Levee

Electric Fence

Net

Resting place

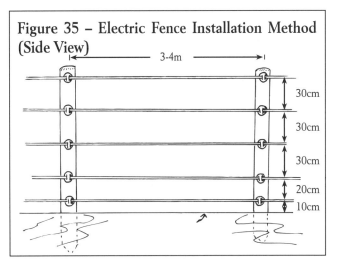

Figure 35 – Electric Fence Installation Method (Side View)

3-4m

30cm

30cm

30cm

20cm

10cm

The electric fence is a psychological fence. Its psychological effect is first exhibited when the predator touches it.

Electric Fence Installation Method 1 (Joint Use of Electric Fence and Net)

Please refer to Figures 34 and 35 for the method of installing an electric fence. In this method, an electric fence and a net are used jointly. It is an orthodox method where the electric fence is used to keep out predators and the net on the inside is used to prevent the ducks from escaping.

The main point is to install the electric fence above the water surface inside the paddy field. This way, the electric shock is doubled, since the electricity is conducted by water. It is also easier to install the fence here since the water surface is flat and the water prevents growth of weeds.

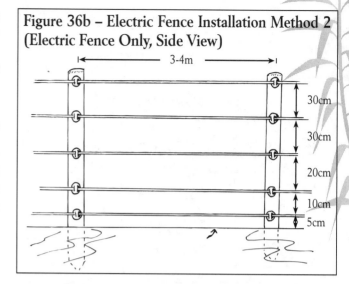

Figure 36b – Electric Fence Installation Method 2 (Electric Fence Only, Side View)

Electric Fence.

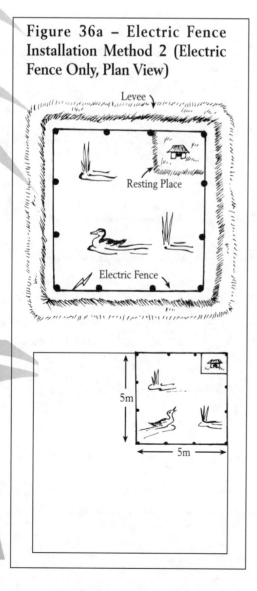

Figure 36a – Electric Fence Installation Method 2 (Electric Fence Only, Plan View)

In my newest method of installing the electric fence, shown in Figures 36a and 36b, I place the bottom wire just 5 cm above the water surface. This is to keep the ducks from getting out and weasels from getting in. When the Aigamo ducklings are swimming in a group, and the one at the front touches the wire, all the ducklings scurry away in a big hurry. Nonetheless, there are cases in the beginning that the ducklings escape by going under the wire. In such cases, I place a 30 cm high corrugated vinyl sheet around the inside of the levee. This also prevents water leakage.

How the Electric Fence Works

Electric fences sold in Japan use a 12 volt power source to send a 0.3 second pulse of nearly 10,000 volts once every two seconds. Either of two power sources can be used: a DC battery or an AC current from the power company. In Japan, there is no danger of humans being killed by such an electric shock.

v. Crows

Are there crows in your country? In Japan, crows are a major enemy of ducks. There are various methods to deal with crows.

a. Fishing Line

Fishing line is strung taut across the paddy field at a height of 1.2 - 1.5 meters and an interval of 2-3 meters. The crows will try to fly into the paddy field, but will hit their wings against the fishing line. The crows will escape frantically with injured wings. It just doesn't pay for them to try to get in. Even if they are lucky enough to get into the paddy field unharmed, they will hit their wings against the line when flapping to fly out.

Differing from other methods, this is an effective method that causes real damage to the crows. They will never get "accustomed" to it.

b. Hanging Up a Dead Crow

This method is also effective for about two weeks. It is no longer effective after the crows get used to it.

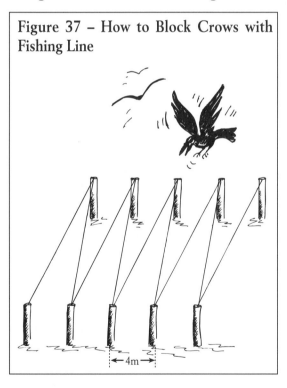

Figure 37 – How to Block Crows with Fishing Line

←4m→

IX. Rice Production

1. Special characteristics of rice growth under the Integrated Rice and Duck Farming system

The appearance of rice grown in duck paddies is

The Water is Muddy in the Paddy Field.

different than that of rice grown in regular paddies. Overall the plant stalks are more heavyset and the leaves branch out in a fan-like shape, as if trying to reach toward the sun. The water in the field is muddy, like strong cafe au lait.

The growth of the rice itself varies depending on the ducks. It is therefore necessary to innovate one's own method of rice production suited to the Integrated Rice and Duck Farming system.

2. Various kinds of Integrated Rice and Duck Farming

Currently there are various forms of Integrated Rice and Duck Farming taking place in villages around Japan and other Asian countries. In Asia's farming villages there are many people engaged in Integrated Rice and Duck Farming on plots of about 3 a.

In Japan there are individual farmers with plots of over 10 ha. who are employing this farming system.

The utilization of ducks in rice farming is being attempted by various methods, e.g., use of ducks just for weeding in conventional rice production; releasing ducks into the paddy field about one month after transplantation; planting large rice seedlings so that ducks can be released into the paddy field three days after transplantation; taking the ducks back to a shed every night and letting them graze in the paddy field during the daytime only; use of ducks in combination with direct sowing of rice; moving "weeder ducks" from one paddy field to another; etc.

Rice production techniques vary widely depending on the objective and way of thinking. Integrated Rice and Duck Farming is not a new technique to be applied uniformly everywhere, but one which makes use of the particular conditions of the fields under cultivation. Nor does it have a uniform sense of values. Each farmer devises his own form of agriculture according to his own values (objectives), ultimately bringing enjoyment to his/her work.

3. My Purposes for Growing Rice

i.   Organic agriculture completely without chemicals . . .   I do not use chemical fertilizers, herbicides, or any other sort of agricultural chemicals.
ii. Ecosystems based on natural cycles and sustainability . . . .   I try to depend on foreign materials as little as possible and try to use the natural potential of the paddy fields creatively.
iii. Using the diverse productivity of the paddy fields . . . .   I see my fields as a place to grow rice, ducks, and other aquaculture products.
iv. Big results with minimum labor . . . .   Intensive rice production without working too hard.
v.   Fun . . . .   Rice farming which is enjoyable.
vi. Increased yield technology . . .   While fulfilling the above conditions, achieving a better yield of better-tasting rice than standard local rice cultivation.

4. Appropriate Images for Integrated Rice and Duck Farming

My ancestors battled against weeds with fire and water — fire to burn fields, and water to submerge their fields and transplant seedlings. In order to confront such flourishing weeds as barnyard millet and galingales, they grew large rice seedlings in nurseries, and transplanted them into paddies covered with water. Submerging fields helped control the proliferation of weeds to some extent, and also helped maximize the size difference between the seedlings and the sprouting weeds.

Integrated Rice and Duck Farming is a means of passing on this wisdom of our ancestors.
Growing sturdy rice plants is the lesson we can glean from this.

One should therefore insure the following:
use no fertilizers —> plant large seedlings —> space the planted seedlings well apart—> release ducks into the fields as soon as possible —> reap the effects of the ducks —> the seedlings should flourish, be thickset with wide stems, and tiller well —> the subterranean roots should be well-developed —> the seedlings should be well exposed to sunlight —> they should be able to withstand typhoons and be resistant to pests —> they should have thick stems and large ears —> large harvest.

normal spacing of rice seedlings in Japan: 20-22 hills/ square meter
sparse spacing of rice seedlings in Japan: 11-14 hills/ square meter
normal spacing of rice seedlings in Southeast Asia (Vietnam): 45-54 hills/square meter

In Southeast Asia, seedlings are planted 2-3 times as densely as in Japan

5. Actual yield

It has been nearly twenty years since I started engaging in completely organic agriculture. For the ten years before I was introduced to the ducks I was out in the paddies nearly every day in the summers pulling out weeds by hand. At that time I was cultivating about 1.7 ha of rice.

During those ten years I was losing the battle against the weeds. I even had fields producing as little as three bales (=180 kilograms of dried, sifted, husked brown rice) of rice per 10 ares. Compared to neighboring fields using the standard chemical fertilizers, herbicides and other agricultural chemicals, my all-natural fields seemed barren.

And then I discovered the ducks, and with their help my rice began to grow. Before this I had been using compost and fermented organic fertilizer to grow "organic rice," but as I watched the ducks swimming freely around the paddies, I lost interest in going out into the fields to spread fertilizer.

In recent years what I have been most interested in is how many bales of rice I can harvest from extremely natural rice fields which make use of nitrogen-fixing plants like Chinese milk vetch and azolla without any inputs of additional materials.

It has been kindly pointed out to me that "if this form of rice production is continued over a number years, the crops will gradually sap the soil of its nutrients, impoverishing the land and causing a smaller yield. It is therefore necessary to use fertilizer and compost to replenish the soil." Yet from my observations of my own fields, the soil has only gotten richer over the years.

My way of thinking is that the weeds are building the soil. Weeds sink their roots deeply into the ground to absorb minerals. At the same time, they use sunlight, water and carbon dioxide to make organic matter. During the Fall, Winter, and Spring, therefore, I grow nitrogen-fixing plants like Chinese milk vetch and other weeds in those rice fields which do not have to support a second crop. Then in late May I plough everything under as deeply as possible.

The actual yield in 1996 was 647 kg* of unpolished rice per 10 ares.

This was from a field which also contained ducks, azolla and fish (loaches).

(*Note: Yields in Japan are measured as the dry weight of sifted (to remove small grains), husked brown rice.)

Ducks' Gift: A splendid rice tussock.

Table 16 – Harvesting Results of Integrated Rice and Duck Farming in 1991

No.	Location	Grower	Plot Type	Rice Type	Transplanted	= Paddy rice x 1.25 sifted brown rice kg/10a
1-1	Keisen-cho	Furuno	control	hinohikari	18 June	180
1-2	Keisen-cho	Furuno	duck plot	hinohikari	18 June	407
2-91	Keisen-cho	Furuno	control	ogonbare	20 June	363
2-2	Keisen-cho	Furuno	duck plot	ogonbare	20June	465
3	Keisen-cho	Furuno	duck plot	ogonbare	16 June	472
4	Keisen-cho	Furuno	duck plot		17 June	385
Kaho-gun, Iizuka City and Yamada City	All rice types				Average yield 383	

Table 17 – Yields in 1992 (Investigated by Mr. Motoyasu Noai, Kaho Agricultural Extension Center)

	dry unhulled rice	unsifted brown rice	husking yield*	sifted brown rice	rice screenings	yield of sufficient size grains
Duck Plot	607kg/ 10a	502 kg/10a	82.7%	432kg/ 10a	13.9%	90%
Duck Plot with muddy water	768kg/ 10a	619kg/10a	80.6%	513kg/ 10a	17.2%	91%

* husking yield = unsifted brown rice (kg)/dry unhulled rice (kg)

The average yields of rice farmers in my area is 383 kg/10 are. Generally, it is only meaningful to compare the yields of integrated rice and duck farming with those of conventional rice farming of the same locality. The yields from my duck fields are equal or superior to those of conventional plots in my area. However, in Japan as a whole, the yields from integrated rice and duck farming are probably somewhat less than those from conventional rice farming (due to lack of experience). It is clear that integrated rice and duck farming increases yields in other Asian countries.

6. Can one expect a good harvest from any field?

I do not mean to assert that one can adopt the Integrated Rice and Duck Farming system to any field and suddenly have a good yield without using fertilizer. The fertility of the land will always be fundamental. No matter how many ducks you put on it, infertile land may well not produce a substantial yield without the use of fertilizer. Using Chinese milk vetch, azolla, compost and other organic fertilizers in combination with ducks will, year by year, enrich the soil and increase production.

7. My practice of raising rice in Japan

I do not imagine that Japan's modernized rice production methods, as is, will be very useful in your respective countries. Nonetheless, I'd like to address those parts of the production process which are relevant to agriculture in Asia and Africa.

i. <u>Growing a variety of crops.</u>
For twenty years I have been searching out kinds of rice suitable for organic farming. Presently, I am growing four or five kinds in my 1.4 ha. of paddy fields. I cannot state indiscriminately which varieties are best suited to Integrated Rice and Duck Farming. This will ultimately depend on conditions of the environment, society, economic state and history within each particular country or region, as well as personal preferences. I can, nonetheless, offer the following conditions.

– Rice seedlings which have sturdy leaves that stand straight
Integrated Rice and Duck Farming works best with varieties of rice whose leaves are thick and stand up straight from the time that they are planted. Such plants can support the presence of ducks earlier.
– Farming with a minimum of fertilizer
In principle my Integrated Rice and Duck Farming system operates without fertilizer and so it is very important to select suitable varieties of rice.
– Rice which will not fall over
The effects of the ducks should produce rice plants with thick, sturdy stems and large ears. For this reason I choose kinds of rice which does not easily fall over.
– Resistant to disease
Although ducks help protect rice by eating weeds and harmful insects, they cannot eat molds or other fungi that attack rice plants. For that reason I guard against disease by adequately spacing* the rice plants and choosing rice which is resistant to disease.

Note: Appropriate spacing varies greatly depending on the local conditions:

a) Normal spacing of rice seedlings in Japan: 20-22 hills/square meter
b) Sparse spacing of rice seedlings in Japan: 11-14 tussocks/square meter
c) Normal spacing of rice seedlings in Southeast Asia (Vietnam): 45-54 tussocks/square meter
d) In Southease Asia, seedlings are planted 2-3 times as densely as in Japan.)
e) Flavor

No matter how organic the production process, all is pointless if the rice does not taste good. Different kinds of rice will have different flavors.

Large seedlings grown in Transplantable pots.

Stages in Azolla Breeding

Azolla is a water plant which hosts symbiotic blue-green algae that fix atmospheric nitrogen
See Page 61

Introduction of azolla to the main paddy field - first azolla is grown in an area enclosed by corrugated plastic sheets
See page 69

The corrugated plastic sheets are removed after the rice plants have grown somewhat
See Page 69

Stages in Duck Tillage & Loaches hiding from Ducks

Immediately after releasing ducks
See Page 78

Two weeks after releasing ducks

Loaches thriving under the azolla
See Page 76

Varieties of Azolla & Harvesting of Loach

Loaches captured
after draining the
paddy fields

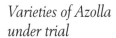

Varieties of Azolla
under trial

Azolla in the rice
field early in growth

Rice Growth and Soil Changes

*Azolla has increased
to 3 tons per 10 a
See Page 71*

Rice plants from (left to right):
a. *conventional plot (use of
   chemical fertilizer, pesticide,
   and herbicide; from a nearby
   relative's paddy)*
b. *control plot*
c. *duck plot*
d. *duck plot (rice plants planted
   early and water kept
   constantly muddy)*
See Page 30

*"F-effect" results in
three-layered soil
structure
See Page 30*

ii. Growing seedlings

With the Integrated Rice and Duck Farming system, it is best to use seedlings which are as large and sturdy as possible. Ducks should be released among the medium or large-sized rice seedlings as soon as possible. How are seedlings prepared in your country? I grow large seedlings in transplantable pots until they are forty to fifty days old. These have thick roots, and even without fertilizer start putting out thick new roots from the day they are transplanted. They grow dark green leaves and have surprising ability to tiller. Even with spaced planting, 36 plants are plenty for 3.3 m² of land. My Integrated Rice and Duck Farming system has reached a new level of stability with the introduction of potted seedlings.

iii. Separating seed-rice using salt water (with a specific gravity of 1.15)

Seed-rice is selected using salt water with a specific gravity of 1.15, to assure the growth of healthy seedlings. When I use seed-rice collected from my own fields, from one-third to one-half of the seed-rice floats to the surface. Though it seems rather wasteful, I carefully select the best grains for use in order to prevent the generation of sick seedlings — the great enemy of rice growing. This is the first step of organic rice production.

How can you achieve a specific gravity of 1.15? In Japan we use a hydrometer, which is quite an easy tool to use. I suggest you inquire about them at universities or laboratories in your country.

iv. Puddling and Levelling (carefully)

Puddling and levelling means using a tractor (cow or horse) to break up soil clods and level the surface of their paddy field.

In your country do people plough their fields and transplant rice seedlings, or do they sow directly? Puddling and levelling is an important procedure in the Integrated Rice and Duck Farming system. It serves the following purposes.
–   to level the surface of the paddy field for systematic planting and weed prevention
–   to prevent leakage of water
–   to bury germinating weeds before they begin to take root
–   to improve the survival rate of the rice seedlings

–   to soften the soil to make it easier to transplant seedlings

The Integrated Rice and Duck Farming system advocates puddling and levelling as uniformly as possible in order to prevent weeds. If the surface of the soil is uneven and there are undulations of the land, barnyard millet and weeds will soon begin to grow on the higher ground. In contrast, seedlings on lower ground will be in danger of being inundated. Ducks will also tend to congregate here, causing your seedlings to disappear and creating a pond-like area in the field.

Recently I have been experimenting with "bird tillage" and transplanting in untilled paddy fields. I let ducks loose on water-covered paddies before planting, prior to puddling and levelling the field with a tractor.

Transplanting seedlings – ducks can be released even at this stage.

v. Planting

I always try to transplant rice seedlings in my fields as soon as possible after puddling and levelling. The reason for this is that barnyard millet and weeds begin to germinate and grow quickly soon after the field is flooded and puddled.

In Japan the planting density is generally about 60 hills per 3.3 m² plot. Using widely-spaced planting, however, my Integrated Rice and Duck Farming system requires between 45 and 36 hills per 3.3 m2 plot. These plants usually are transplanted with about two or three stalks per hill. They are large, mature seedlings that are 40 to 50 days old, are about 25 cm long, and have 5 or 6 large leaves.

After planting is completed, the water is kept at between 10 to 15 cm in depth to discourage the weeds.

vi. Fertilization

In recent years Integrated Rice and Duck Farming has in principle aimed for completely compost-free rice-growing without the use of basal dressing, topdressing or other forms of compost. Yet for me this is based on a number of premises:

- rice should be planted after a secondary crop (of green manure, etc.), or
- the Chinese milk vetch and weeds should be tilled under before the Spring, or
- azolla should be introduced to the land, or
- the land should be "bird tilled" prior to planting or grazed by ducks for some time after harvesting.

If the soil is not rich I apply about two tons of compost per 10 ares in the Fall and Winter (once only).

To this extent I have actually given my rice plants very little compost in recent years. As I have said, the nitrogen, phosphorus and potassium (N.P.K.) derived from duck droppings is about 20% of the standard amount applied in customary rice-growing in Japan.

So why does the rice grow under these conditions? From my observations the rice gets bigger whenever it rains. It must be that the nitrogen in rain water is being utilized. On the other hand it may well be that the N.P.K. and other nutrients normally left unused in the soil are being used due to the full-time ploughing and muddying effect. Of course, duck droppings are not dumped on paddy fields all at once like compost and other kinds of fertilizer. That they come in small amounts everyday must be very beneficial to the rice plants, increasing the efficiency of use. It has been reported that through Integrated Rice and Duck Farming, the amount of fertilizer used has been halved in certain cases, and other Asian countries (Vietnam) as well.

vii. Water management

The basis of water management in Integrated Rice and Duck Farming is not allowing the muddy water to leak out of the rice paddies.

To do this one must pile up more dirt on low levees to make them higher. The levees must then be firmly sealed. In principle there is no exchange of water, and that water which is lost must be replaced.

I maintain a depth of 10 to 15 cm soon after planting, which preserves the seedlings and controls the weeds. The seedlings are mature and tall enough to thrive in the deep water.

Water is generally kept at this depth until the ducks are released in the fields. Just before they are released, the depth must be adjusted to a level where they can both float and walk. This is about 5 to 7 cm.

After three or four weeks the weeds will disappear from the paddies. After that time any water level is possible. From about 45 days before the rice comes to ear I keep the level relatively shallow (under 5 cm).

Doing this promotes tillering. After that I maintain that same water level until the rice comes to ear, at which time I drain the field naturally.

After that, I dry and rewater the fields on one-day intervals.

Chapter Three

The Potential of Integrated Rice and Duck Farming Throughout Asia

I. Integrated Rice and Duck Farming can Be done without an Electric Fence

I wonder what your impressions are after reading Chapters One and Two. Perhaps you have felt that Integrated Rice and Duck Farming, which uses electric fences, nets, etc., is not possible in many regions where such equipment is too expensive or hard to obtain.

Integrated Rice and Duck Farming is possible anywhere that there are paddy fields and ducks. Many farmers are enthusiastically engaging in Integrated Rice and Duck Farming in South Korea, Vietnam, the Philippines, Laos and other countries with pretty good results.

When I first went to Vietnam in 1994, I asked about dogs. I was told "if dogs attack the ducks, people will capture and eat the dogs." As this shows, I believe there is a long history of interaction between humans and dogs in your country, which is different from that in Japan. Many different methods of Integrated Rice and Duck Farming are being developed to adapt to local conditions.

In areas with many duck predators, it is possible to dig a pond around or on one side of the paddy field, or to reverse one's thinking by having "duck dogs" (like sheep dogs which protect sheep) guard the ducks. In areas where duck robbers are active at night, appropriate measures should be taken.

At first, please make a small experimental plot in your paddy field, and try out Integrated Rice and Duck Farming following the instructions in this book as much as possible. If it proves effective, improve the technique to adapt to the circumstances in your country.

Asia has a long history and tradition of working with waterfowl — ducks, geese and Muscovy ducks. I have learned a lot myself from the Asian culture of interaction with waterfowl. Many interesting things become apparent when integrated rice and duck farming is looked at from a wider Asian perspective.

II. Rural Asia

Barefoot young men quietly ploughing small paddy fields using water buffalo beneath a burning sun. Young girls exchanging chatter as they pick up rice seedlings. Men driving flocks of hundreds of ducks with nothing but a bamboo pole. Young boys returning home in the evening riding on the backs of water buffalo.

A man herds ducks in Vietnam.

In the rural areas I visited in Asia, the villages were always surrounded by water channels and ponds in which ducks were swimming happily. The people drank the water of the channels, and in the evening used nets to catch fish there, which they ate for dinner. There were also plenty of small fish in the paddy fields.

III. The "developing" countries of Asia are the "advanced" countries of sustainable recycling agriculture.

Visiting these rural areas in Asia was for me a very nostalgic experience. At the same time, I became very aware of just how much Japan has lost in the process of modernizing its agriculture. Up until the early 1960's in my village in Japan, we were also surrounded by water channels and ponds, and there were many fish in the channels and paddy fields.

However, even in the rural areas of Asia, in step with the infiltration of the market economy, the use of chemical fertilizers and agrichemicals is growing.

If this continues, and the developing countries follow the same path of "agricultural modernization" as Japan, the basis of existence, a flourishing natural environment, will be destroyed. Further, as economic ties strengthen, the ability to catch fish of the paddy fields, drink the naturally flowing water and generally lead a self-sufficient farming life, will be lost.

In recent years, modernized agriculture in the advanced countries has reached a dead end and sustainable agricultural methods are attracting a lot of attention. Noting this world trend, the Japanese Ministry of Agriculture, Forestry and Fisheries has also begun to advocate agricultural styles which promote the conservation (preservation) of the environment.

When one takes a good look at the situation, the industrially advanced countries which are now beginning to promote environmentally conservationist agriculture should themselves be adopting a more modest posture in learning from the several thousand years of traditional Asian farming. In a sense, we can say that the developing countries of Asia are the true "advanced countries of environmentally conservationist agriculture."

In spite of this, it is now becoming extremely difficult to maintain traditional lifestyles in the rural areas of Asia, which are already experiencing the introduction of the market economy. It is also a fact that many Asian farming people are simply not receiving an adequate diet.

In the villages I visited in northern and central Vietnam, rice was eaten for only ten months of the year. The people got by on cassava and sweet potatoes for the remaining two months, and it should be noted that Vietnam is the third largest rice exporting nation in the world.

In this situation, however much the industrially advanced countries may preach to the developing countries about "the importance of environmental conservation," while enjoying the consumption of most of the world's mineral and energy resources, and living on over-adequate diets, their argument will lack persuasiveness. What Asia really needs now is "practical agricultural techniques which will conserve the environment and increase yields."

Interestingly, in contrast to Japan, integrated rice and duck farming has been creatively adapted to local conditions, and its use is spreading as a technique for improving yields in Vietnam and the Republic of Korea.

In Vietnam, by combining the ubiquitous duck with rice cultivation, rice yields have been increased by 15 to 30%, while at the same time producing duck meat, reducing labor inputs for weeding, reducing costs for artificial fertilizers and agrichemicals, thus increasing income to 150 to 200% of previous levels. In fact, the effectiveness of this technique and the necessity for its introduction is greatest in the developing countries of Asia where weeding has been carried out by hand and by very strenuous labor.

Integrated rice and duck farming in Vietnam.

Integrated rice and duck farming is just one small example of the kinds of farming techniques, harmonizing the workings of nature and humanity, which can come about through exchanges of traditional agriculture between Asian countries. The establishment of a real sustainable recycling form of agriculture is for Asia, and indeed for resource-poor Japan, one of the most urgent conditions for Asian coexistence and self-reliance in the twenty first Century.

IV. Comparison of Duck Behavior in Traditional Asian Duck Paddy Field Grazing versus Integrated Rice and Duck Farming

Is it reasonable to say that traditional Asian duck paddy field grazing is the same as Integrated Rice and Duck farming?

In the sense that "waterfowl are allowed into paddy fields," traditional Asian duck paddy field grazing and Integrated Rice and Duck Farming are exactly the same.

In my view, the main purpose of traditional Asian duck paddy field grazing appears to be stockbreeding, in other words having the ducks eat the weeds, insects and river snails of the paddy field and to get exercise. The emphasis does not seem to be placed on encouraging the growth of the rice plants, as it is in integrated rice and duck farming.

In Asia, ducks are introduced into paddy fields with no fences and are allowed freedom of movement. This method does not limit the area of activity of ducks with nets and so on, and so is suitable for providing the ducks with a natural supply of feed for consumption. However, this method lacks a mechanism to provide continual positive influence on the rice plants.

In traditional Asian duck paddy field grazing (in Vietnam, China and the Philippines), the ducks can cross the ridges between paddy fields and move "horizontally" from field to field pecking at the leaves of the rice plants in search of food, mainly insects.

In integrated rice and duck farming, firstly the ducks move around in a limited area eating the tasty insects on the leaves of the rice plants and around the base of the tussocks. Next they eat the grass seeds and weeds floating on the surface of the paddy field. Lastly, they poke their beaks into the mud in the paddy field, or stir it up with their webbed feet, eating the insects or grass seeds that they find there.

In other words, as well as moving horizontally about the plane of the restricted area, they also move downwards in a perpendicular direction. The effect of the ducks is thus exerted overall, continually, and

evenly by this three-dimensional movement. Thus it seems to me that although traditional Asian duck paddy field grazing results in a certain degree of suppression and elimination of weeds and insects, the effectiveness of nutrient supply and water-muddying is probably not sufficiently strong.

An extremely formalistic representation of the comparison of duck behavior would be as follows.

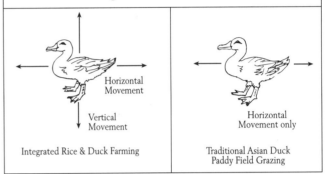

Figure 38 – Comparison of duck behavior between Asian duck paddy field grazing and integrated rice and duck farming.

V. Traditional Asian Duck Paddy Field Grazing

In A Luoi District, Hue Province, central Vietnam, 10- to 15-day-old duck chicks are introduced into the paddy fields around a month to a month and a half after rice seedling transplantation. The period of one to one and a half months is apparently to allow the rice plants to develop strong roots. During this period, the rice farmers of this area carry out weeding by hand and also spray the rice plants with pesticides.

The duck farmers allow their ducks into the paddy fields owned by the rice farmers. If the owner of the field wants to apply some kind of agrichemical, he informs the duck farmer, who then removes his ducks from the field.

Thus, duck paddy field grazing is not carried out in anticipation of favorable growth of the rice plants, but just for duck grazing.

In Kampong Cham Province in Cambodia, I talked with an old man who has a tent on the banks of a lake and keeps 1600 ducks.

"When the ducks begin to lay eggs, they can be allowed into the paddy fields. There's a lot of feed for them in the fields. If the ducks are smaller than that, they move in groups and push the rice plants over, so they mustn't go in the paddy fields. The ducks can go in the fields a month and a half after seedling transplantation. When the ears appear, the ducks are not allowed in the fields. The ducks are put in the paddy fields in the morning, and in the lake in the afternoon."

In Bukidonon on Mindanao island in the Philippines, duck farmers are asked to put large ducks into flooded paddy fields before seedling transplantation in order to eliminate golden snails.

Ducks Being Herded in Cambodia.

In Asia, ducks are usually kept in the house while small, and allowed in the paddy fields when they become larger. The reason is very simple. While the ducks are small they eat very little, but when they grow larger they consume a large amount of feed, so they are kept at home while small and are taken to the paddy fields to eat natural feed when they become larger.

VI. A Unique Creative Development

Through my friends, I have been invited to many parts of Asia and have met many farmers and researchers. Recently, a combination of traditional Asian duck grazing techniques and my integrated rice and duck farming has resulted in unique and interesting developments.

Integrated Rice and Duck Farming in Haiphong, northern Vietnam.

1. [Paddy field fencing] Simple bamboo fence with nets. Generally, dogs do not eat the ducks. Dogs which eat ducks have been eliminated through eating by humans.
2. [Planting density of rice] 45-54 hills per m². (Twice or three times that of Japan.)
3. [Number of ducks grazed per unit area] 45-75 ducks/10 ares. (Twice or three times that of Japan.)
4. [Timing of initiation of duck grazing] 7 to 18 days after seedling transplantation.
5. [Age of ducks at initiation of duck grazing] 7 to 28 days
6. [Duck variety] traditional Vietnamese small duck

VII. Integrated Rice and Duck Farming and VAC

In Vietnam, there is an agricultural organization called VAC VINA. VINA means "Vietnam" and VAC is taken from the first letter of the Vietnamese words for orchards (vuon), fishponds (ao) and livestock pens (chuong).

VAC is a farming method that has been practiced in the Red River delta from ancient times. In the delta region, houses were built on raised earth mounds, the hole from which the earth was taken becoming a pond around which livestock were kept and vegetables were grown. VAC is a traditional Vietnamese farm management complex which has combined these various elements in an organic fashion. This has

The VAC System.

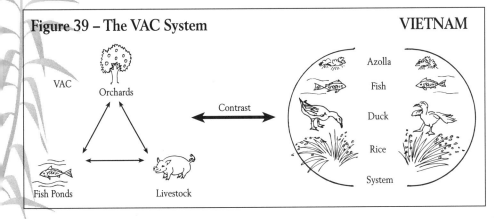

Figure 39 – The VAC System

VAC · Orchards · Fish Ponds · Livestock · Contrast

VIETNAM

Azolla · Fish · Duck · Rice — System

accounted for an important part of the improvement in the farming economy and nutrition.

I thought it very strange that paddy fields were not included in the VAC system, and I asked the Director of VAC VINA Central why this was. The Director answered that vegetable cultivation is five times more profitable than growing rice.

In fact, according to how you look at it, integrated rice and duck farming is one way of integrating rice cultivation into the VAC system, from which it is currently excluded. (See the AFDR Method) This could be quite a significant development in Vietnam.

VIII. Integrated Rice and Duck Farming in Vietnam

Around 40 million ducks are now being kept in Vietnam, making that country second only to China in the number of ducks kept. It is said that there is a strong correlation between the degree of environmental preservation and the distribution of ducks. So if ducks are being kept, it must be because there exists a suitably flourishing natural environment.

In March 1994, we visited Vietnam under a Japan International Volunteer Center (JVC) program. The purpose was to initiate exchanges with farmers and researchers concerning integrated rice and duck farming.

The SAP Center in Haiphong City had begun to allow duck chicks to graze in a paddy field, with the cooperation of JVC, after having seen my books and a video (the video is now available in Japanese, Vietnamese, French and English).

This was the beginning of the Vietnamese integrated rice and duck farming.

Currently, this method is spreading rapidly in Haiphong Province in the north, Hue Province in central Vietnam, and in Dong Thap and Ben Tre Provinces in the south. There are very enthusiastic people in all of these areas. Through experiments and guidance of the Director of the SAP Center in Haiphong City, Mr. Tran Van Nhu, nearly 300 farming households are trying out the method. A 15% increase in yield and a doubling of income has been achieved. Haiphong City has approved and is supporting integrated rice and duck farming as an environmentally friendly agricultural technique. I think that, having begun as a project of an NGO (JVC) and a farmer's organization, receiving support from a city is a deeply significant achievement in Vietnam. As can be seen in the Table 18, integrated rice and duck farming is now spreading in northern Vietnam as a technique for improving yields as well as income.

Increased Yields also Achieved in Hue Province

In central Vietnam there is a city called Hue, which has a beautiful river flowing through it. Hue is the capital city of Hue Province, and also the old capital of Vietnam. In this province, the mountains come down almost to the sea, and the land is poor, making this one of the most impoverished provinces of Vietnam.

Since 1993 I have been invited to Hue four times. There is an agricultural technician called Mr. Ai who works in the Hue Province Crop Protection Agency. He used to carry out instruction on IPM (Integrated Pest Management), but because of his enthusiastic experimental research and efforts in promoting integrated rice and duck farming, he is now known as Mr. "Aigamo" (Duck) Ai. Mr. Ai's data in Table 18 also clearly show the economic effectiveness of this method.

Combination with direct sowing in the south.

In southern Vietnam, the area of agricultural land per household is large and most rice cultivation is carried out by direct sowing. Up to now, the activities of the

Table 18 – Comparison of Expenditures in Duck Areas and Conventional Areas

Table by Tran Van Nhu, Director of SAP Center (per sao, units:dong)

Category	Calculation	Duck Plot	Conventional Plot
Expenditure			
Seed Cost	3 kg x 3000	9,000	9,000
Ploughing (Labour)	3 people x 10,000	30,000	30,000
Transplanting (Labour)	1.5 people x 10,000	15,000	15,000
Compost	200 kg x 150	30,000	30,000
Phospate Fertiliser	10 kg x 1,000	10,000	10,000
Nitrogen Fertiliser	5 kg x 3,000		15,000
Weeding (Labour)	2 people x 10,000		20,000
Pesticide			15,000
Ducks	15 birds x 2,500	37,500	
Duck Feed	2.5 kg x 15 x 2000	75,000	
Fence Cost	120,000 / 6 seasons	30,000	
Total Expenditure (A)		236,500	144,000
Income			
Duck Plot:	150 kg x 2,000	300,000	
Conventional Plot:	130 kg x 2,000		260,000
Duck Meat	14 kg x 13,000	182,000	
Gross Income (B)		482,000	260,000
Net Income (B-A)		245,000	116,000

Notes: "Conventional Areas" are ordinary paddy fields nearby.
1 sao = 360 m², 100 dong = 1 Japanese yen

JVC have generally been concentrated in the poorer agricultural areas of northern and central Vietnam rather than in the rich Mekong delta in the south.

However, since the Japan-Vietnam Aigamo Symposium was held at Can Tho University, Can Tho in 1995, developments appropriate to the situation in the south have been taking place in Dong Thap and Ben Tre Provinces.

In direct sowing rice cultivation in Japan, duck grazing is not possible until the rice seedlings have grown quite large, about one month after sowing. During this one-month period, weeds also become quite large. Thus, in Japan, the paddy field is flooded and "bird tillage" or

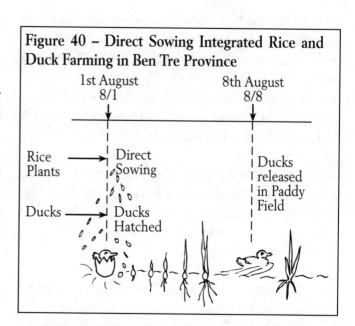

Figure 40 – Direct Sowing Integrated Rice and Duck Farming in Ben Tre Province

"double ploughing and leveling" is carried out before direct sowing in order to suppress weed appearance.

Directly sown rice plants and ducks in Ben Tre.

IX. The Significance for the Small Subsistence Farmers of Asia

Here I would like to look at the significance of integrated rice and duck farming for the small subsistence farmers of Asia with Vietnam as the main example.

1. Savings in material inputs such as Chemical Fertilizers, Agrichemicals and Herbicides.

Compared with Japan, the economic significance of this is large. As calculated in Table 18, the cost of chemical fertilizers, agrichemicals and herbicides amounts to about one-third of the price of the rice. According to my calculations, this is about three times as much as in Japan.

This is probably due to the differences in agriculture and industry in developing and industrially advanced countries.

2. Alleviation of hard labor for Weeding

In Vietnam, large numbers of people go out in the fields and weed by hand. I was told that one young man can weed 1 sao (360 m^2) in eight hours. This needs to be carried out two or three times for each crop.

If the ducks, which are in the surroundings anyway, are used in combination with rice cultivation, liberation from this hard weeding labor is possible.

The significance of this is great when compared with Japan or the Republic of Korea, where nearly all rice cultivation relies on the use of herbicides.

3. Effect of Suppression and Elimination of Insect Pests

In rural areas that I have visited in Vietnam and in other Asian countries, it seems that damage by insect pests is more serious than in Japan. When I first introduced integrated rice and duck farming to other Asian countries I was unsure as to whether the expected effect would appear or not due to differences in timing of arrival and the life cycle of the insects when compared to Japan. However, it now appears that the effect of

What is the situation in the Mekong delta? As shown in Figure 40, the area has a tropical climate, the temperature is high, sunlight is plentiful and the rice plants grow at a speed unthinkable in Japan. In about the first week after direct sowing, small chicks in their first week are allowed into the paddy fields.

From what we saw and heard, rice plants in directly sown fields grow to have four leaves and are about 21 to 24 cm in height 15 days after sowing. With this, duck grazing is possible.

According to the extension worker Mr. Tuyen, when seedling transplantation was being carried out, it was normal practice to allow ducks into the paddy fields, mostly for the purpose of having them eat the insects.

However, since the spread of direct sowing, ducks are not allowed into paddy fields directly sown for fear that they will trample the rice plants. Driving through the Mekong delta, I often saw paddy fields surrounded by net fencing, but I was told that this was "to keep out other people's ducks." In other words, ducks are treated as pests in directly sown paddy fields. Now, that notion has been completely reversed with the introduction of integrated rice and duck farming.

Tuyen pointed out "We always used to put ducks in the paddy fields, so integrated rice and duck farming is just a matter of surrounding the field with a net fence." An apt saying from the duck country of the Mekong delta!

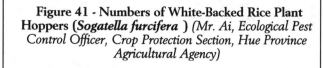

Figure 41 - Numbers of White-Backed Rice Plant Hoppers (*Sogatella furcifera*) *(Mr. Ai, Ecological Pest Control Officer, Crop Protection Section, Hue Province Agricultural Agency)*

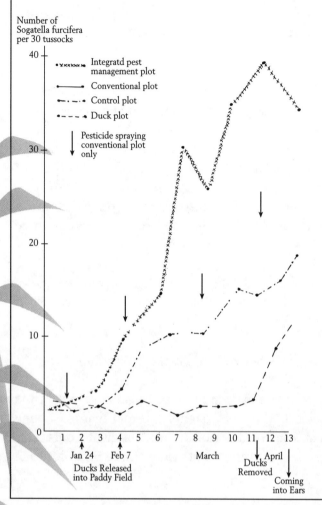

The important feature of Figure 41 is that compared with the IPM areas, conventional areas, and control areas, the density of Sogatella furcifera in the duck areas was considerably lower.

It seems that in traditional Asian duck grazing the ducks were allowed to graze in the paddy fields when infested with insect pests. Compared with this, ducks are in the paddy fields all the time up to coming of ears in integrated rice and duck farming. The ducks intercept the first insect pests as they arrive and do not allow them to lay eggs on the rice plants, and that is the reason for the superior insect pest suppression and elimination effect.

4. Increased Yields Realized

An increase in yield has been realized through the implementation of integrated rice and duck farming in several Asian countries. For example, in Savannakhet, Laos, trials by Toshio Ikehara of the Japan Overseas Cooperation Volunteers (JOCV) have resulted in a tripling of yields. Yields in Haiphong, Vietnam, have risen 15 to 30%.

Although in Japan rice produced by integrated rice and duck farming sells for about twice the normal price of rice, the price cannot be marked up in Asian countries, at least at present. The increase in yield itself is the important factor.

In Japan, IRDF rice can be sold at higher price since it is organic, safe and tasty. In most developing countries in Asia, the majority of the population are farmers who grow rice to eat themselves (South Korea is an exception). Many farming families do not have enough to eat. So IRDF rice is seldom evaluated higher just for being organic. In the developing countries of Asia, IRDF is a method for reducing material and labor inputs and increasing yields. In Japan and South Korea, it is valued as a method of organic farming.

5. Greatly reduced damage from Rats

Rats do not pose a problem to rice seedlings standing in paddy fields in Japan. In Vietnam, however, the rats are large and they cause very great damage to rice crops. Duck grazing has had a large effect on rat damage in Vietnam. There are two reasons for this effect.

The Hue Net Hypothesis: Paddy fields where ducks were grazed were surrounded by net fences and that is

suppression and elimination of insect pests by the ducks has been quite remarkable in all of the countries where it has been tried.

Director Nhu of the SAP in Haiphong reports that suppression of insect pests that attach to the outer surface of the stem (beetles [kamemushi, pentatomidae], rice leaf rollers (*Cnaphalocrecis medinalis*), locusts) is very good, but that a certain amount of damage has been seen from insect pests that bore into the inside of the stem, such as larvae of rice skippers (*Parnara guttata*). However, compared with control areas, the damage was very limited (about one-fifth compared with control areas).

Mr. Ai in Hue has investigated the appearance of the white-backed rice plant hopper (*Sogatella furcifera*), and his results are shown in Figure 41.

why there was no damage to rice plants from rats. The nearby farmers will probably erect net fences around their fields to keep out rats from the next crop.

The Haiphong Excreta Hypothesis: The reason for the elimination of damage from rats was that the rats do not like the smell of the ducks' excreta. The reason why small ducklings were attacked by rats was that the smell of the excreta had not yet covered the whole paddy field. When the ducklings grow larger and the smell has spread across the whole field, the rats no longer attack the ducks and rat damage to rice plants is eliminated.

Recently, Mr. Tuc of Vietnam informed me of something I had never thought of: "You refer to rats merely as "rats," but there are two types of rats- it is the brown [sewer] rats that attack the ducks, and the black [roof] rats that eat the rice plants." That explained the problem to me. Previously, I had no idea that there were two different kinds of rats in the paddy fields.

6. Protecting both the Natural Environment and the Tradition of Duck Grazing

The problems of the natural environment in the rural areas of Vietnam and Indonesia are very serious. One method for alleviating this situation is to implement integrated rice and duck farming, as it combines creatively the use of paddy fields and ducks, thus making full use of the properties of nature, ducks and the paddy fields.

X. Duck Farming goes to Asia

Dear Mr. Takao Furuno,

"How are you? I was a participant in the symposium with Japanese and Vietnamese farmers on integrated rice and duck farming that was held at the University of Can Tho (in the Mekong delta). Quite a long time has passed since then, but I have been constantly thinking about integrated rice and duck farming. This is because, for the sake of the perpetual health and continued existence of humanity, I would like to develop a method of rice cultivation that does not use fertilizers or agrichemicals. The continued existence of humanity is my fervent wish. ... If a symposium including all the provinces of the Mekong delta were to be held with your support, I am sure this farming method will spread to a much wider area."

This letter, in Vietnamese, arrived at my house in the fall of 1995. It was sent by Le Phu Tuc, a farmer in the Dong Thap Province of the Mekong delta. The land of Dong Thap Province is generally low-lying wetlands which are flooded by the Mekong River in September every year.

In 1994, a "Japan-Vietnam Aigamo Symposium" was held at Can Tho University in the Mekong delta with the cooperation of the JIVC (Japan International Volunteer Center. Known as JVC in Japan, but internationally the abbreviation normally used is JIVC.) After the symposium, Mr. Tuc and I really hit it off, and had a long discussion about farming over several glasses of beer.

Mr. Tuc put his brand new hat on my head saying, "It suits you, Furuno. You look just like a Vietnamese farmer." He gave me the hat as a present.

It was from this man that I had received the letter above. As a request from one Asian farmer to another, I could not refuse. I had neither money nor time, but spurred on by his sheer enthusiasm I said to myself, "I'll go!" This is how I always set out on my trips to Asia. This was my fourth visit to Vietnam.

My first trip to another Asian country was in May 1992. At that time I accompanied a group led by Professor Manda of Kagoshima University on a trip to rural areas in China and Taiwan for research and exchanges on the use of ducks in paddy fields.

In a village we visited in Xing'an County in southern China, several streams ran through the village, and there were small ponds behind the warehouses, where ducks and geese swam around. The paddy fields nearby were all flooded with water and the duck chicks were allowed to graze in them. Humans, rice plants, water buffalo and ducks were coexisting, supported by the natural abundance of the river. The technique of allowing farm ducks to graze in the paddy fields arose naturally in this environment, and this tradition, backed up by a thousand years of experience, still continues today.

Since that time, thanks to my connection with the ducks (aigamo), I have visited rural areas in several countries in Asia including the Republic of Korea, Malaysia, Indonesia, Vietnam, Cambodia, the Philippines, and also Tanzania in Africa.

As far as I have been able to ascertain, the history and current situation of duck paddy field grazing in Asia is as shown in Table 19. I have differentiated between the traditional Asian method of allowing ducks into paddy fields with no fencing and integrated rice and duck farming.

Before I had visited several areas of Asia I had imagined that the roots of duck paddy field grazing were in China, but after actually visiting rural areas of Asia I found that anywhere where there were ducks and paddy fields, the ducks would find their way into the paddy fields and be playing around in them. I realized that it was probably more natural to assume that rather than having been invented in one place and spread from there, the traditional technique of allowing waterfowl to graze in paddy fields had arisen spontaneously (naturally) throughout the rice-growing areas of monsoon Asia.

With Mr Tuc.

Table 19 – History and Current Situation of Duck Paddy Field Grazing in Asia

China [PRC] (1992)	The agricultural classic "Yuan Chao" states that, "Duck Paddy field grazing was invented through practice by agricultural labourers in southern China in the 13th or 14th Century." I have actually witnessed in Xing'an Country, Guangxi Province, farmers carrying duck chicks to the transplanted paddy fields in bamboo baskets for grazing.
Republic of Korea (1992, 1993, 1994, 1996, 1997)	According to research stations and universities, there was no tradition of duck paddy field grazing in Korea. At present, Integrated Rice and Duck Farming is being introduced to several areas through the efforts of the members of the Right Agricultural Association including Choi Sung Kyu and Kim Dai Nyun who received training at my home, and Hong Soon Myung of Pool Moo Agricultural High School. Integrated Rice and Duck Farming has also been the subject of research at several national research institutes. Rice produced using this method has also received government approval as "Organic Rice No.1". My book "Aigamo, Banzai" was published in Korean in May 1997.
Indonesia (1993)	At all of the universities and research stations I visited I was told that in Indonesia the only duck grazing was in the empty fields after harvesting, and that has been carried out for many years. I was told of a nomadic people called the Sontoroyo who travel through the rice-growing areas by driving their ducks from one harvested paddy field to the next near Chelbon in west Java. However, on Bali I witnessed ducks grazing in paddy fields with young rice plants (before coming to ears).
Malaysia (1993)	Could not confirm use of ducks at all.
Vietnam (March and November 1994, 1995, 1996, 1997)	There were two opinions: One was that ducks have been allowed to graze in paddy fields with young rice plants (before coming to ears), in harvested fields and in water channels since ancient times. The other was that ducks were thought to be injurious to rice plants. In fact, duck chicks were allowed to graze in the paddy fields with young rice plants (before coming to ears) in the rural areas around Haipong City in northern Vietnam. Presently, with the support of the JVC and through exchanges between farming people, integrated rice and duck farming is now spreading around Haiphong in the north, Hue in central Vietnam and the provinces on Dong Thap and Ben Tre in the south. In 1997, Haiphong City began subsidies for integrated rice and duck farming. In the Mekong delta, a combination of integrated rice and duck farming is steadily spreading in the area.
Cambodia (1996)	Duck paddy field grazing continues to be carried out, mainly for duck raising. Trials of integrated rice and duck farming are being carried out by Mr Chatterjee of JIVC Cambodia and by the Japan Oversease Cooperation Volunteers.
The Philippines (1997)	On Mindanao, large ducks were allowed into the paddy fields about one month before seedling transplantation in order to eliminate golden snails. Xavier University Sustainable Agriculture Center and Bukidonon farmers are scheduled to begin trials with integrated rice and duck farming. Good results are expected for suppression and elimination of weeds and insect pests.

*Year of visit by Takao Furuno

In addition, Japan Oversease Cooperation Volunteers are carrying out trials with integrated rice and duck farming in Laos. The method is spreading around Vientiane through the efforts of Mr. Sato of the FAO.

In Papua New Guinea, OISCA is carrying out trials with integrated rice and duck farming.

Trials of integrated rice and duck farming were being carried out at the JICA Farm in Moshi, Kilmanjaro Provice (Tanzania) which I visited on a JICA program in 1996.

Chapter Four

New Developments in Integrated Rice and Duck Farming

I. The New Technique of Integrated Rice, Duck, and Azolla Farming

With the introduction of azolla, integrated rice and duck farming became an unlimited "sustainable recycling" system. I would mainly like to mention here the appeal of azolla, its ecology (biology), and how it helped to bring about a new development in integrated rice and duck farming.

1. What is Azolla?

i. My Meeting with Azolla

I first learned about azolla, a very interesting floating weed that is capable of fixing nitrogen directly from the atmosphere, in a letter I received in 1993 from Professor Iwao Watanabe, a retired professor of the Faculty of Biological Resources at Mie University. Professor Watanabe is a world authority on azolla who worked for 16 years at the International Rice Research Institute at Los Baños in the Philippines. There is at IRRI a living collection of over 500 lines of azolla gathered by Prof. Watanabe from all over the world. When I read Prof. Watanabe's letter I immediately felt a strong interest in the use of azolla as a "green feed" for ducks.

ii. What is Azolla?

Does azolla also grow in your country? The Japanese common name for azolla is "akaukikusa." It is a fern-like plant that lives in water, a "floating weed" that flourishes in paddy fields, water channels and ponds. There are seven types of azolla in the world, and it is widespread throughout temperate and tropical zones.

Table 20 – Azolla Species and Features By Natural Habitat

Species	Sub-species	Natural Habitat	Features
A. pinnata	subsp. asiatica*	Asia, Japan	low production, poor nutrition
A. pinnata	subsp. pinnata	Oceania	contains little nitrogen
A. pinnata	subsp. africana	Africa, Madagascar	low production, poor nutrition
A. nilotica (Tetrasporocaria nilotica)		Central Africa	Can get as large as 15cm. A bit weak
A. filiculoides**		Central & North America	High production. Weak to high temperatures.
A. rubra**		New Zealand	Poor nutrition Weak to high temperatures
A. microphylla***		Central & South America	High production. Strong to heat. Good nutrition
A. caroliniana		Central, South & North America	Strong to heat
A. mexicana		Central & South America	Strong to heat

*Includes A. imbricata (Japanese: akaukikusa) native to Japan. ** A. japonica (Japanese: ooakaukikusa) native to Japan is close to A. filiculoides and A. rubra. A. rubra is considered by some to be a sub-species of A. filiculoides. ***A. microphylla, A. caroliniana and A. mexicana are difficult to distinguish from one another. Nearly 500 lines of Azolla are kept alive at IRRI. In Japan, Mr. Nobuyuki Shiomi of the Research Institute of Osaka Municipal University keeps some of these varieties.

iii. Agricultural modernization in Japan has brought azolla to the brink of extinction.

It is very unusual to see azolla in Japan nowadays. It was apparently seen very widely until the 1950's in paddy fields with poor drainage. At the time, azolla was considered to be a nuisance "paddy field weed" with great reproductive strength.

However, with the improved paddy drainage from farmland improvement and development, the improvement in water channels, and the use of herbicides, azolla began to disappear. Azolla appears to be especially sensitive to herbicides.

It has been said for many years that small fauna such as small fish, shrimps, diving beetles (*Cybister japonicus*), and killifish have now disappeared from Japanese paddy fields, but plants have also been disappearing.

Azolla is one of these victims of agricultural modernization. It seems that there is no history of the use of azolla in Japan. The combined use of azolla and ducks in paddies in integrated rice, duck, and azolla farming constitutes a romantic attempt at revival and resuscitation.

2. Azolla's great Characteristics

Aoukikusa (green floating grass - *Lemna paucicostata*) is often seen in Japan's paddy fields today. Despite being a kind of floating weed, its characteristics are quite different from azolla.

i. Superior Nitrogen-fixing Ability

Azolla has small double leaves, one above the other. There are small pores on the underside of the upper leaf. In these pores live symbiotic blue-green algae (ransou) (cyanobacteria), which fix atmospheric nitrogen and supply it to the azolla.

In return, since the blue-green algae cannot fix carbon by photosynthesis, it is supplied with carbon from the azolla on which it lives.

Azolla's nitrogen-fixing ability is extremely good, being about the equivalent of legumes. Under good conditions, azolla is said to be able to fix three to five kilograms of nitrogen per hectare per day.

ii. Strong Powers of Propagation

As well as the ability to fix atmospheric nitrogen, azolla also shows amazing powers of propagation.

Under suitable conditions, it is said to be able to double its fresh weight in two to three days.

In an investigation I carried out in my own paddy fields, six kilograms of azolla placed in a 25-are paddy on 5th May 1995 had spread over the whole paddy and weighed a total of seven tons by 20th June. This represents a growth of 1166 times in 45 days. Since 2 to the power of 10 is 1024, then the mass of the azolla must have been doubling about every three days.

3. The Historical use of Azolla in Asia (Traditional Utilization)

In the past, azolla has been considered in Japan mainly as a "paddy field weed," and hardly any attempt to make positive use of it is known.

It seems that azolla has been made use of from ancient times in other Asian countries such as China and Vietnam.

i. Use of Azolla as Green Manure in Paddy Fields

In southern China and northern Vietnam, azolla of high nitrogen content has been long used as a green manure in paddy fields.

The traditional methods of azolla utilization are:

a. Introduce azolla into the paddy field one or two months before transplantation of rice seedlings and allow the azolla to spread. Just before transplantation plough the azolla under for use as a basal dressing.
b. Introduce azolla between the rice tussocks and allow it to spread. At weeding time, plough the azolla under as a top dressing.

ii. As a Weed Suppressor

When azolla covers the whole surface of the water in a paddy field, it shuts out some of the light, thus preventing weeds from sprouting.

The question is whether the azolla will be able to completely cover the surface of the water before weeds can get their heads above the waterline. In the temperate climate of Japan, where azolla is introduced into the paddy field at the time of seedling transplantation, this is thought to be rather difficult.

iii. As a Feed for Animals
There is a long history of the use of azolla in Asia as a feed for pigs, ducks, and freshwater fish.

It is apparently used in the Philippines as a feed for the golden snail.

4. Growing conditions for Azolla

i. Water
Azolla is a floating weed, and cannot grow without water. It usually grows in several centimeters of water in a paddy field. Azolla can also absorb nutrients, especially phosphates, directly from the soil through its roots. Azolla thus prefers relatively shallow water.

In Japan's temperate climate, azolla will continue to grow after water has been drained from a paddy field by pushing its roots into the soil.

In winter, the azolla can survive if it is kept in a frost-free state by a covering of straw or grass, but the azolla may wither and die if very dry conditions prevail in early spring.

ii. Wind
As azolla is a floating weed, it will tend to be blown to one side of a paddy field in the wind.

Especially in the early stages, when the azolla has not yet covered the whole water surface and the rice plants are still small, the azolla may be blown to one side of the field. Azolla does not grow well when it is concentrated in a small area.

iii. Temperature
Growing temperatures for azolla are said to be between 15°C and 30°C.

According to my experience in Kyushu, in the south of Japan, azolla seems to be particularly prone to frost damage.

However, frost does not occur in a vinyl greenhouse, and even if the water in which the azolla is floating

freezes at night, the azolla will recover perfectly well when it warms up during the day.

I have tried growing several varieties of azolla experimentally, and have found that azolla will grow strongly during April in a vinyl greenhouse, and in the open air from May. From August onwards, heat causes growth to slow.

iv. Light
Azolla generally turns red under conditions of stress. In Japan, when the light is too strong in the summer, and when it is too weak in the winter, azolla definitely does turn red.

However, interestingly, when azolla is in the shade, away from direct sunlight, it turns green.

v. Phosphates
As azolla usually floats on the surface of the water, it has difficulty in absorbing phosphorus from the soil.

The supply of phosphates is the biggest problem in the growth of azolla.

vi. Insect Pests
Azolla's greatest pest is the *Pyralidae*. This "pest" appears when azolla increases too quickly and becomes overcrowded.

The *Pyralidae* construct a tunnel-like nest in the azolla and eat it away. If not treated, the azolla will turn brown and wither in two to three days.

In addition, slugs and golden snails also like azolla very much and will eat away at it.

5. Integrated use of Azolla - Integrated Rice, Duck and Azolla Farming

Looked at from the point of view of integrated rice and duck farming, azolla has great appeal. You could almost say that azolla and integrated rice and duck farming were made for each other.

The complexity of relationships between rice, ducks and azolla is shown in Figure 42.

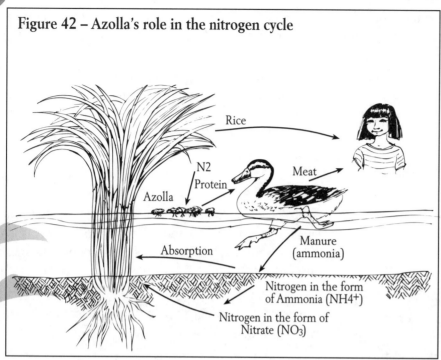

Figure 42 – Azolla's role in the nitrogen cycle

Rice

N2

Protein

Meat

Azolla

Absorption

Manure (ammonia)

Nitrogen in the form of Ammonia (NH4+)

Nitrogen in the form of Nitrate (NO3)

absorbing nutrients from the soil through its roots.

Similarly, as azolla is a floating weed and does not grow upwards like normal weeds, it does not prevent any light from reaching the rice plant.

Azolla thus has these "special features" which make it possible to <u>cultivate rice and azolla together simultaneously in companion planting.</u>

In much the same way as ducks are used, it is possible to grow azolla in paddy fields in a way that surpasses monoculture.

Nitrogen that azolla fixes from the atmosphere passes along the chain from atmosphere -> ducks -> rice -> humans.

At the same time, the rice, ducks, and azolla interact together to promote each others' growth.

The various functions of the paddy field, the rice and azolla become integrated with the various abilities of the ducks to result in a highly integrated system of utilization. This is a development which has arisen from conventional (traditional) azolla utilization techniques.

6. Various Positive Effects of Azolla

As a preparation for discussing the practical side of integrated azolla, duck, and rice farming, I would like to take a look at the positive effects of azolla use from several different perspectives.

<u>i. The Effect on the Rice Plant</u>
<u>a. Azolla can be cultivated simultaneously with rice.</u>
The floating weed azolla utilizes a slightly different growing space from the rice plant. Azolla usually floats on the water in the paddy field and absorbs essential nutrients from the water. It fixes nitrogen from the atmosphere.

Because of this, azolla differs from normal weeds in that it does not compete with the rice plant by way of

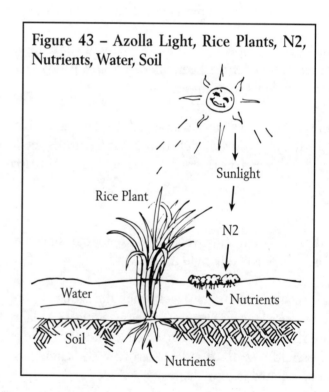

Figure 43 – Azolla Light, Rice Plants, N2, Nutrients, Water, Soil

Sunlight

Rice Plant

N2

Water

Nutrients

Soil

Nutrients

<u>b. The Positive Effect of Incorporating Atmospheric Nitrogen into the Paddy Field</u>
In a fertile paddy field, it is actually possible to achieve yields roughly equivalent to those achieved in that particular area by customary practice (using chemical fertilizers, agricultural chemicals, and herbicides) just by allowing ducks into the paddy field. I have direct experience of this in several paddy fields each year - as described in Chapters One and Two

However, in a paddy field of low fertility, it is generally not expected that yields approaching those achieved in that area by customary practice will be achieved by simply allowing ducks into the paddy field. In that case, one would conventionally apply compost, organic manures, or use a green manure such as Chinese milk vetch (*renge, Astragalus sinicus L.*) as an off-season crop in order to supplement soil nutrients.

However, azolla can bring atmospheric nitrogen directly into the paddy field where the rice has been planted. This brings an amazing sustainable recycling capability into the picture. Instead of humans inputting external materials into the paddy field, azolla uses the natural power of the paddy field to bring atmospheric nitrogen to it automatically.

ii. Positive Effects on Ducks
a. Cultivating Duck Feed among the Rice Plants.
By allowing ducks to graze in the paddy field, the number of weeds will become visibly reduced in three or four weeks. This weeding effect is a natural consequence of duck grazing.

Alternatively, from the duck's viewpoint, it means the feed is becoming scarce. Although this is fine from the point of view of growing rice, from the point of view of raising animals (stockbreeding) it is not so good. This contradiction can be overcome by the use of azolla, an aquatic feed crop with strong powers of propagation and a high degree of nitrogen fixing capability.

In paddy fields with ducks, azolla is a perfectly sufficient green feed. Thanks to the introduction of azolla, ducks are never seen feeding on rice plant leaves following the disappearance of weeds from the paddy field.

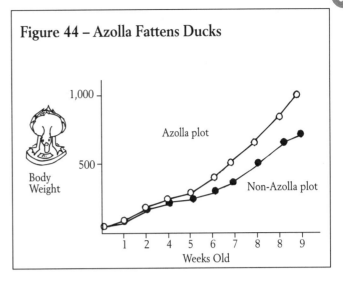

Figure 44 – Azolla Fattens Ducks

b. Azolla shows its strength as an "Aquatic Feed Crop"
Azolla performs better than expected as an aquatic feed crop.

This is true not simply because the ducks fatten as they eat the azolla. It is thought that the nitrogen fixed by azolla becomes the main source of nutrients for small aquatic animals (such as midge [*yusurika*] larvae [also known as "bloodworms"]) to multiply quickly. These are then eaten by the ducks, which grow fat.

Table 21 shows the results of an investigation of the contents of ducks' stomachs carried out with staff of the local farming extension center over the last few years. It is quite clear that the ingestion of midge larvae (bloodworms) is extremely large in fields growing azolla as compared to non-azolla fields. There are various types of midges, all in the *Chironomidae* family. The Japanese term used (yusurika) here is a generic term referring to midges in general.

Figure 44 shows the results of a comparative

Table 21 – Small Fauna Eaten by Ducks (Contents of Gullet, examined 21 July 1995)							
	Weight of contents	midge larvae	plant hoppers	springtails	spiders	beetles	midge adults
Azolla Plot	107.1 g	233	18	4	1	1	9
Non-Azolla Plot	35.6 g	33			1	1	2

investigation of the body weight of ducks grazing in azolla and non-azolla field areas carried out by Prof. Yoshiro Kishida of Okayama University. Clearly, the body weight of ducks in azolla areas increases faster.

The positive effect of azolla as a direct and indirect feed is undeniable.

The conventional use of azolla is to plough it under and allow it to decompose either before seedling transplantation or at weeding time. This is a good way to make use of the nitrogen fixed by the azolla, but doesn't this waste the protein, amino acids, vitamins, energy and so on contained in the azolla which decompose when the azolla is ploughed under?

All of these are used effectively when the azolla is eaten by ducks.

iii. Positive effects for Azolla

A quick glance at this situation seems to tell you that the azolla gains nothing from this system, as it is just eaten by the ducks.

Things are not so simple. In fact, the ducks also have a very good effect on the azolla.

a. Prevention and removal of Insect Pests

The Pyralidae larva is a big enemy of azolla. In Japan, if azolla grows too thickly it will suddenly turn brown and begin to wither.

This is because azolla is attacked by a mould-like disease when eaten by the Pyralidae larvae. This problem is especially serious in tropical regions.

However this problem is very quickly solved when ducks are used in combination with azolla as the ducks perform a wonderful service of ingesting the Pyralidae larvae.

When young ducks (chicks) are let loose among the azolla, they first swim around eating all the insects from the top of the azolla.

b. Ducks prevent overcrowding of Azolla

During early stages, when the amount of azolla is still quite small, there is the worry that the ducks will eat all the azolla in the paddy field.

Interestingly, duck chicks at first swim around eating the insects on the azolla and rice plants.

After a while the azolla begins to propagate rapidly. The azolla actually grows faster than the ducks can eat it, but because the ducks are ingesting suitable amounts of azolla, it can spread nicely over the field without becoming overcrowded.

c. The "full-time ploughing and muddying effect" for Azolla

Professor Watanabe explained to me that:

'The azolla floats on the surface with its roots dangling in the water. Because of this structural arrangement, azolla's absorption rate of phosphates is low. However, when ducks are allowed into the azolla paddy field, they stir up the soil with their beaks and webbed feet and muddy the water.

This "full-time ploughing and muddying effect" causes phosphate in the soil to dissolve in the water. The phosphate is then probably absorbed by the roots of the azolla, which then propagates as a result.'

Azolla in a control area partitioned off with corrugated sheet so that the muddied water could not seep in, showed a red color for a long period. This was probably through lack of phosphate.

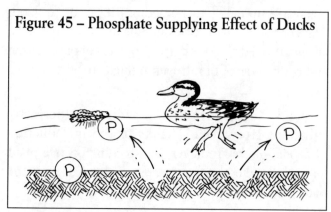

Figure 45 – Phosphate Supplying Effect of Ducks

d. Evening Out and Expansion

Azolla is susceptible to wind and rain, and in early stages when the azolla does not yet cover the whole paddy field, strong winds and heavy rain can cause the azolla to be blown into one corner of the field. It is not good for the healthy growth of azolla to be too overcrowded. However, when the wind dies down and a flock of ducks is allowed to swim around, the azolla will be spread throughout the field and will resume propagation.

7. The Practical Side of Integrated Rice, Duck and Azolla Farming

With the introduction of azolla, integrated duck and rice farming entered into a new phase and became very interesting. At the same time, it brought new possibilities in the use of azolla, which had been in stagnation due to the introduction of cheap chemical fertilizers made available by the market economy.

These were the new possibilities of the "combined use" of azolla. I would like to discuss here the practical side of integrated rice, duck and azolla farming from the point of view of "rice farming" and "stockbreeding".

i. The Various Systems for the use of Azolla
a. The Azolla + Rice (A+R) System — Traditional use of Azolla

The traditional use of azolla involves a simple combination of rice and azolla as a "green manure" for the rice or as a weed suppressant.

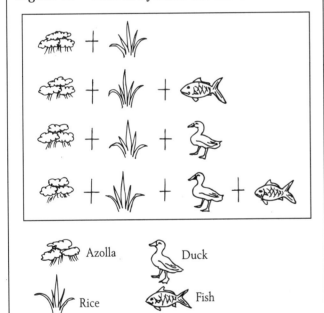

Figure 46 – Various Systems for the Use of Azolla

Azolla
Duck
Rice
Fish

This application of azolla has been used since ancient times in southern China and northern Vietnam.

In Vietnam, the azolla was ploughed under before seedling transplantation.

In China, ploughing under before seedling transplantation, and cultivation of azolla between the rice tussocks after transplantation for later ploughing under were both carried out.

However, in the late 1980's, the advent of the market economy and the availability of cheap nitrogen fertilizers, caused this traditional use of azolla, which requires a higher level of labor input, to begin to disappear quickly. The use of chemical fertilizers has ended up replacing the traditional use of azolla.

b. The Azolla + Rice + Fish (A+R+F) System
I read the following in a paper by Prof. Iwao Watanabe:

> *The Institute for Agricultural Science of Fujian Province has a state-approved special center for research on azolla. In the mountainous areas of Fujian Province, there is a tradition of fish breeding in paddy fields, but in villages where the fish productivity is low and chemical fertilizers are not widely available, the research center is developing and promoting a method of using azolla as feed for the fish. This helps to cut down on expenditures for fertilizers and feed, and also provides extra income through the sale of fish. The kinds of fish used are grass carp, tilapia, and carp (and more recently catfish). The kinds of azolla used are A. pinata, A. filiculoides, and A. microphylla, (which have differing types of resistance to temperature) and their hybrids.*
>
> *Rice plants are cultivated using a broad ridge method, ensuring that the azolla between the ridges receives sufficient light. A small pit is dug in one part of the paddy field for oxygen supply and for adding extra feed.*
>
> *It is thought that azolla first captures nitrogen. The fish then eat the azolla, and then the rice plants absorb nutrients from the excreta of the fish. In an experiment using azolla marked with 15N, a 39% loss of nitrogen occurred when azolla alone was cultivated with rice plants, but in an azolla + rice + fish system the nitrogen loss was cut to only 15%. Nitrogen loss was found to be reduced in the paddy field with the fish by just the amount of nitrogen the fish assimilated. Thus nitrogen fertilizer efficiency was improved, allowing inputs of fertilizer to be reduced.*

According to paddy field tests carried out by the Rice and Wheat Research Section of the Institute for Agricultural Science of Fujian Province in 1988, in addition to obtaining a similar rice yield (9 tons per hectare in two growing seasons), the azolla + rice + fish system also produced an income of 4 tons per hectare of fish as well as reducing chemical fertilizer input to less than a fifth when compared with rice monoculture.

Furthermore, a reduction in the incidence of sheath blight (Rhizoctonia solani) and plant hoppers in the azolla + rice + fish system made it possible to reduce inputs of agrichemicals.

Thus the azolla + rice + fish system, which produces little change in rice yield, but which reduces expenditures for material inputs and also produces extra income through the sale of fish, caused farmers' incomes to rise significantly.

This farming method is now spreading in the Jianning County region of Fujian Province. **99**

(Prof. Iwao Watanabe, *Tropical Agriculture*, 1993)

This long quotation is a good description of the A+R+F method.

c. The Azolla + Rice + Duck (A+R+D) System

At first glance, this method may appear to be simply the A + R + F method described in ii. with ducks replacing fish.

But this would actually be wrong, as ducks are amphibious. In this sense, ducks are fundamentally different from fish, which are active only in the water.

This method represents a higher stage in the combined use of rice, ducks and azolla.

When azolla is introduced, yields of both rice and duck meat increase.

d. The Azolla + Rice + Ducks + Fish (A+R+D+F) System

This method truly is the most comprehensive combinatory use of azolla.

Nitrogen is first fixed from the atmosphere by azolla. The azolla is eaten by the ducks. The duck excreta act as feed for microorganisms, water fleas and plankton, which flourish. These are in turn eaten by the fish.

The rice plants grow by making use of the nutrients provided by the decomposition of the excreta. This is a method which makes efficient use of the natural powers of the paddy field. As far as I can see, this method results in the greatest yield increase of all factors: rice, ducks, fish and azolla.

As can be seen from the above, there are various ways of making use of azolla. The common feature of all of these is that they use the atmospheric nitrogen fixed by the azolla in the paddy field as a nutrient source for the natural growth of rice plants, ducks, fish and so on.

ii. Is Azolla a "Green Manure" or a "Green Feed"?

Is the azolla used in integrated rice and duck farming a "green manure" for the rice plant? Or is the azolla a "green feed" for the ducks? I believe, on balance, it is a "green feed" for the ducks.

In order to use azolla as a green manure (basal dressing) it is necessary to allow water into the paddy field about a month before seedling transplantation and have azolla growing over the whole field before puddling and leveling (shirokaki).

This may be perfectly possible in tropical and sub-tropical countries, but in Japan is generally quite difficult because of water-use and temperature problems.

Thus, as a green manure crop to be ploughed under before seedling transplantation, Chinese milk vetch (*renge, Astragalus sinicus L.*; a legume) has been cultivated in Japan while the paddy fields are still dry.

In integrated rice and duck farming, the "weeds" — "green feed" — which have disappeared due to the "weeding effect" of the ducks are replaced by azolla with its high nitrogen fixing ability and strong powers of propagation.

In this system, azolla is firstly a "feed" for the ducks. Secondly, duck excreta become an effective "green manure" (top dressing).

Azolla is cultivated between the rice plants in a paddy field, and then ploughed under using a manual weeding machine. (Rorezo Jose, Florida Blanca, Philippines — from Prof. Watanabe's book.)

As in the photograph, in the Philippines and in China, azolla which has spread between the rows of rice plants is ploughed under using a manual weeding machine, It becomes useful as a top dressing for the rice plants.

When compared with this, the way that ducks work becomes very clear.
In effect the ducks take the place of the weeding machine and the human who pushes it. Integrated rice, duck and azolla farming is a sustainable recycling system of feed crop cultivation, duck raising (stockbreeding), and rice cultivation all in one beneficial system.

Since it is being used as a "green feed," it is not necessary for the azolla to cover the whole paddy field completely.

iii. The Integrated Rice, Duck and Azolla Farming Calendar

An integrated rice, duck and azolla farming calendar is shown below. This is one method for Japan, a temperate climate. It will probably be quite different from that in tropical and sub-tropical countries.

iv. Preserving the seed Azolla

Where I live, frost falls from November. Usually, if azolla is exposed to heavy frost, it will turn red and wither. Thus I take samples of seed azolla for the following year in August, before draining the paddy fields. Generally, I place about 5 cm of paddy field soil in a 50 cm X 50 cm polystyrene foam container, cover that with about 5 cm of water, and then float the azolla on the water.

Figure 47 – The Integrated Rice, Duck and Azolla Farming Calendar No.1 (Japan)		
Period	Rice Plants and Ducks	Azolla
March, April	Coming of spring	Azolla begins to propagate in the vinyl house.
May	sowing	As frost no longer falls, azolla can be propagated outside.
June	transplantation of rice	Azolla introduced into small area of paddy field separated off by corrugated sheet.
	introduction of ducks into paddy field	
Mid-June		Corrugated sheet surrounding azolla is removed.
August	tillering	As rice plants tiller, visibility between tussocks is reduced. Azolla growth slows and azolla plants shrink.
Mid-Late	August	Rice plant foliage cuts off light, and coupled with consumption by ducks, over 90% of azolla disappears.
End of August	Ducks removed from paddy field, water drained from paddy field intermittently	Remaining azolla puts down roots in the paddy field
October	harvesting	
November		As first frost falls, azolla in the paddy field withers away. Before this happens, seed azolla for the following year should be placed in a vinyl house or in a sunny place indoors.

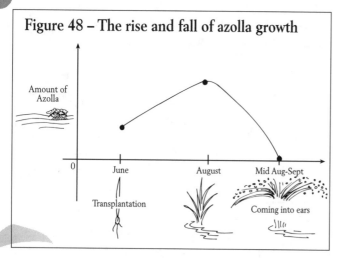

Figure 48 – The rise and fall of azolla growth

Amount of Azolla

0 — June — August — Mid Aug-Sept

Transplantation

Coming into ears

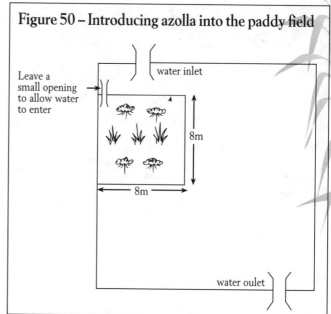

Figure 50 – Introducing azolla into the paddy field

water inlet

Leave a small opening to allow water to enter

8m

8m

water oulet

This kind of preparation is probably also necessary for preservation of seed azolla during the dry seasons in tropical regions. If the seed azolla container is to be left outside, care should be taken that the azolla is not washed away in heavy rains. It is probably a good idea to place the seed azolla under the eaves of a house where it can receive good sunlight, but where it will be sheltered from rain. It is also possible to fix floats to the sides of a small plastic or bamboo sieve, place the azolla in this and then float it in the container mentioned above.

Why is it necessary to partition off an area of the paddy field during the early stages of azolla growth?

    a. At the time of introduction, the amount of azolla is small and if it were introduced directly into the paddy field without partitioning off, it would be spread throughout the paddy field by the wind and rain, possibly to become difficult to find.

    b. If the azolla turns red, it can be effectively helped out by application of organic phosphate fertilizer directly into the partitioned area.

    c. The partitioned area is especially necessary if ducks have already been allowed into the paddy field to graze. It is necessary to ensure that the ducks do not get into the partitioned area before the propagation rate of the azolla exceeds the rate of consumption of the azolla by the ducks.

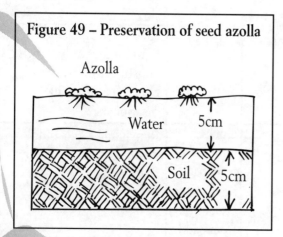

Figure 49 – Preservation of seed azolla

Azolla

Water — 5cm

Soil — 5cm

v. Introduction of Azolla into the Paddy Field
Azolla is introduced into the paddy field as soon as possible after rice seedling transplantation. First, as in Figure 50, an area of the paddy field close to the water inlet is partitioned off with corrugated sheet, and azolla placed in it to begin propagation.

The azolla is placed in this position because as it multiplies and the corrugated sheet is removed, the azolla is allowed to drift and spread throughout the paddy field by the flow of water from the water inlet.

Further, while the rice seedlings are still small, the ducks may swim around energetically in groups among the azolla, and the azolla may get on top of the seedlings, causing them to be submerged. It is necessary to keep the azolla in the partitioned area until the seedlings have grown to a good size.

Of course, the partition is not necessary if the seedlings are large and the amount of azolla introduced is relatively great.

When the azolla has grown so as to completely fill the partitioned area, then the corrugated sheet can be removed.

In my case, this is usually about one to two weeks after introduction of the azolla.

vi. Amount of Azolla introduced

At temperatures over 20°C and in good conditions, azolla will double its mass in three days and increase a thousand-fold in a month.

Based on this calculation and my experience, I usually start by introducing two to five kilograms of azolla per ten ares.

It will be necessary for all of you in your different countries to determine through practice the amount of azolla you need to introduce into your own paddy fields.

vii. Varieties of Azolla

As shown in Table 20 (Chapter Four, Section I.1) there are several varieties and lines of azolla in the world.

As a general rule, a variety resistant to cold, which can grow quickly in the early spring, and a variety which is resistant to summer heat (and may be slower growing in the spring) should be used in combination. The two varieties will then grow in combination, the early spring (low temperature) variety and the mid-summer (high temperature) variety helping each other out.

My Azolla Combination:

Hybrid 4087 (*A. filiculoides, x A. microphylla*) + Ooakaukigusa (*A. japonica*)

However, the following has also been brought to my attention:

" *For the azolla used in integrated rice, duck and azolla farming, varieties such as Azolla japonica are good from the point of view of rice cultivation as they are resistant to cold, propagate well in early spring, are susceptible to heat and thus wither away. The advantage is that the azolla can be used as ear manure (top dressing at panicle formation stage) rather than allowing the azolla to continue on with its nitrogen fertilizer effect into the later stages of rice plant development.* "

viii Limits on the Timing of Introduction of Azolla

I often hear people say they have placed azolla in a paddy field with ducks, but that the azolla has disappeared after a while. If azolla is to be used effectively as a "green manure" and a "green feed," there is a limit on the timing of introduction of the azolla.

After ducks have been allowed into a paddy to graze, paddy field weeds will more or less disappear from view in about four to five weeks. Hungry for green feed, the ducks will completely eat up any azolla that is placed in the paddy field after that time. Basically, the rice plants, the ducks, and azolla should be considered "classmates," the most ideal situation being that they all start off together.

ix. Points to watch in Azolla and Water Management

With regard to azolla growth, there is no necessity to be particularly careful with water management. It is probably best to arrange for the water depth to be slightly shallow (3 cm to 5 cm) as that will help the azolla to propagate faster.

While the rice seedlings are still small, if there is (for example) heavy rain and the water becomes deep, the azolla may get on top of the rice seedling foliage, causing the seedlings to submerge. The rice seedlings could then wither with the muddying effect of the ducks.

Ensuring that the water does not become too deep, planting mature seedlings or large seedlings, and allowing small ducks into the paddy field to graze are all important elements.

x. Azolla growth in Paddy Fields with Ducks

Azolla growth in paddy fields with ducks is shown in Figure 48.

When the azolla is introduced into the paddy field in early June it soon begins to propagate. Roughly one month later the azolla will have spread to cover the whole paddy field (approximately 2 tons per 10 ares). In August, growth stops and the azolla begins to recede. From around mid-August, the amount of azolla becomes noticeably reduced. This is because the rice plant foliage becomes luxuriant, cutting off much of the sunlight between the rice plant rows and tussocks, and the ducks also consume larger amounts of azolla as they grow.

xi. The Behavior of Ducks in the Azolla Paddy Field

According to research carried out at Kagoshima and Okayama Universities, if ducks fed on mixed feed are also given azolla, it is interesting to see that there is an increase in the amount of mixed feed consumed. Apparently, the azolla stimulates and increases the ducks' appetites.

If you actually observe ducks in a paddy field, ducks in an azolla field move around in a calm and composed manner, probably because green feed is in plentiful supply.

This is why in paddy fields with ducks and azolla, when compared to those without azolla, problems often caused by ducks, such as rice foliage eaten, roots dug up, trampled stems and so on, are witnessed far less often.

xii. Yields in Integrated Rice, Duck and Azolla Farming

When azolla is introduced into paddy fields with ducks, the color of the foliage of the rice plant deepens, the stem becomes more stout, and more tillers are formed. This effect is particularly noticeable in relatively infertile paddy fields with poor soil. Why does this happen? It is after all because the nitrogen fixed by the azolla passes through the bodies of the ducks, the excreta becoming nutrients for the rice plants.

Figure 51 shows the amounts of nitrogen supplied by the ducks from azolla.

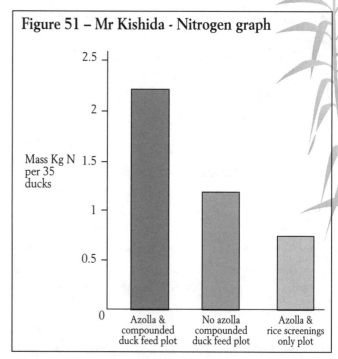

Figure 51 – Mr Kishida - Nitrogen graph

Mass Kg N per 35 ducks

(Assistant Prof. Kishida, *Okayama University*)

Whether a system is a sustainable recycling one or not, it has no meaning if rice is not actually produced. Below are shown rice yields.

II. New Technique: Integrated Rice, Duck, Fish and Azolla Farming

Are there fish living in the rice paddies in your country? Do these fish come and go naturally, or have they been stocked? Unfortunately there are virtually no fish in

Table 22 – Comparison of Yields in Integrated Rice, Duck and Azolla Farming Last Year
(Investigation by Prof. Manabu Katano of Kyushu Tokai University)

	Azolla-	Azolla+	Azolla++
Yield (g/m2)	646 (99)	617 (95)	647 (100)
Hills/m²	12.1 (99)	12.2 (100)	12.2 (100)
Panicle per Hill	32.6 (127)	31.1 (121)	25.7 (100)
Grains per panicle	98.7 (94)	99.0 (94)	105.5 (100)
Panicles per square meter	395 (123)	377 (118)	320 (100)
Grains/m² (a)	38,987 (116)	37,521 (111)	33,760 (100)
% of Ripened Grains (b)	77.6 (100)	72.4 (93)	77.7 (100)
Weight of 1000 grains	21.1 (99)	21.0 (98)	21.4 (100)
No. of Ripened Grains per m² [a x b]	30,254 (116)	27,165 (103)	26,232 (100)

Notes: "Azolla-" is integrated rice and duck farming, "Azolla+" is integrated rice, duck and azolla farming, "Azolla++" is integrated rice, duck and azolla farming where first azolla alone is allowed to propagate in large amounts.

	m²	grains/ear	% of ripened grains	Mass of sifted brown rice per 1000 grains (g)	yield of sifted brown rice (g/m²)
Table 23 – (1995 Data) Rice Yield and Details					
Azolla Plot	254.4	98.3	89.3	21.6	482.3
Non-Azolla Plot	216.8	91.2	87.5	21.5	372.3
Significant Difference	*Yes	*Yes	n.s.	n.s.	*Yes

* = significant at the 5% level, ns = not significant

20 tussocks were sampled and investigated. Results are partly different from those presented at the Aigamo Forum in 1995, but the trend is exactly the same.

modern Japanese rice paddies. The reason for this is agrichemicals, weed killing agents, the consolidation of small paddy fields into large, rectangular-shaped fields geared to mechanized farming, concrete irrigation ditches and other so-called environmental alterations which have accompanied the modernization of agriculture.

But I do have fish living in my rice paddies. Crucians and killifish entered my duck fields through the irrigation ditches and have started to prosper there. Moreover, I have been combining fish (loaches, carp, etc.) with my integrated rice, duck and azolla farming since 1996. These fish are pleasant companions to integrated rice and duck farming and open up the possibility of aquaculture.

1. The viewpoint of creative sustainable agriculture — using your rice field like a pond

You can employ integrated rice, duck, azolla and fish farming to produce rice as well as side dishes in a way that is mutually prosperous to all. Originally rice fields were spaces with this sort of diversified productivity. The modernization of agriculture, however, has targeted single crop, large-scale, labor-efficient methods. The result has been the transformation of paddies into monocultures solely for the production of rice. The consolidation of paddy fields to promote mechanized farming has also turned the landscape of Japanese farming villages into boring, homogeneous spaces.

On one hand, integrated rice, duck, azolla and fish farming is a compounded production technique, entailing growing rice

and raising livestock and aquatic products simultaneously. The rationale behind this method of compound agriculture is inherited from Asian traditional techniques and stands in complete contrast to the concepts of modernization. Namely, the concept is to produce a variety of products within a limited space to achieve maximum overall productivity. But this does not consist of merely assembling all of the components; it consists of allowing all components to influence each other positively in a relationship of symbiotic production. Again, this is not viewing rice fields simply as a place to grow rice, but as "ponds" for growing a variety of products, namely, azolla, rice, ducks and fish.

Rice paddies have incredible production potential. Those that are shallow and have warm water temperatures can sustain quite a variety of aquatic plants and animals. In some Asian combined fish and rice farming systems, a deep pond is dug around the shallower rice paddy and used to raise fish. I have preferred to keep all of my rice paddies shallow and then chosen to stock them with easily-cultivated loaches. Integrating cyclical sustainability and compounding techniques in this manner is an attractive alternative for the Twenty-first century, the century of communal living. I would like to creatively transform areas of homogeneous rice production into ones which are prosperous and complex, similar to Asian markets themselves.

Figure 52 – Conventional Paddy Fields = Only Rice Plants

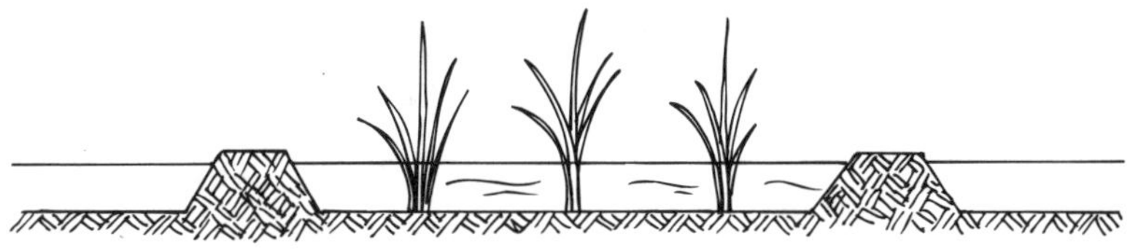

Figure 53 – Paddy Field as a Pond - The azolla, fish, duck, rice ecosystem

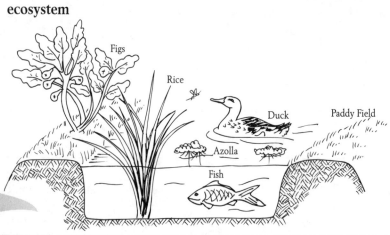

rice. Simultaneously, they also generate a multitude of nutritious water fleas, *Orthocladius akamusi*, tubificid worms, and plankton for the fish (loaches) to eat. The fish droppings then nourish the rice as well. This, the Integrated Azolla, Fish, Duck, Rice Farming System food chain, has the following three distinctive features.

The first is high economic efficiency. Rice, ducks and fish can be raised with a small outlay of capital and, if this investment goes well, income will exceed that of monocultural rice farming considerably.

Figure 54 – Integrated Duck, Rice & Fish Culture

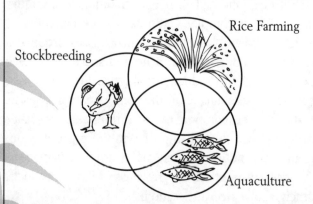

The second is the cyclic sustainability of the system.

This means that individuals have only to contribute a little leftover rice. After that, the azolla becomes the primary producer of food for the system.

The third is simple management. In other words, one can produce rice, breed stock and aquaculture products within the rice paddy "pond" with a minimum of human labor.

3. Learning from Asian methods

In order to to clarify the strong points of Integrated Rice, Duck, Azolla and Fish Farming, as compared to other techniques, I would like to examine the Yu Tang fish pond system of the Chinese Zhu Jiang Delta and the traditional Vietnamese combined rice, fish, duck system.

2. The Integrated Azolla, Fish, Duck, Rice Farming System

If you look at Figure 55 you will note that this is a virtually self-sustaining system of airborne nitrogen, carbon dioxide, solar energy and water. All that is required from outside of this system is a little leftover rice for duck food. Except for this small rice contribution, everything is supplied naturally — in other words, free. Nitrogen-fixing azolla propagates quickly above the waterline, combining with weeds, bugs, other aquatic plants and animals and the leftover rice to become a source of protein and fodder for the ducks.

The ducks' droppings, in turn, become nourishment for the

Figure 55 – Material Cycles of Azolla + Loaches + Ducks + Rice Plants

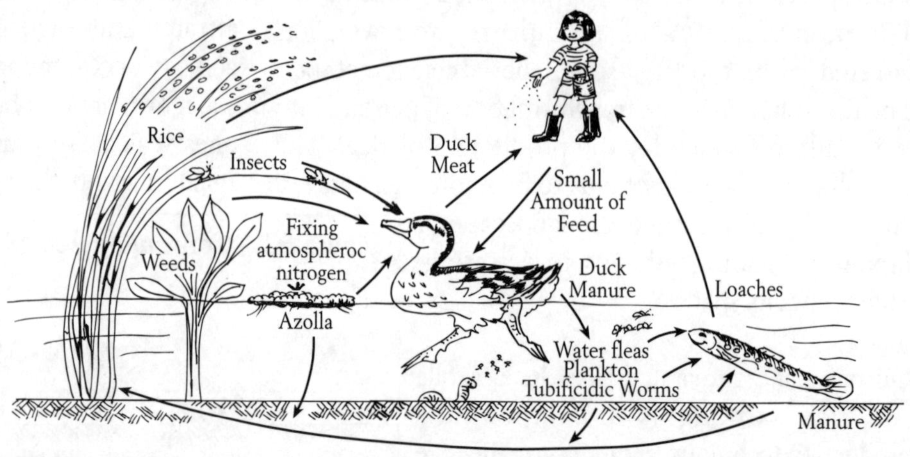

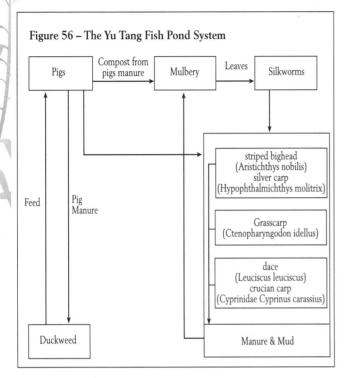

Figure 56 – The Yu Tang Fish Pond System

are used as food for silkworms and the fish (along with the silkworm droppings), in this way becoming useful for two purposes and creating ten times the agricultural profit."

ii. The Vietnamese Combined Rice, Fish, Duck System

Mr. Lu from the Dong Thap Province attended the Integrated Rice and Duck Farming Workshop which we held in 1995 in the Mekong Delta area, the granary of Vietnam. He was engaged in the method illustrated in Figure 57, which is an adaptation of a traditional way of combining fish and rice.

This method involves digging a 1.8 meter deep trench around the paddy field. Not only does this trench serve as an area to raise fish, it is a barrier which protects the ducks from stray dogs and other predators.

The fish live in this water when water levels are low; when the water levels rise the fish can also swim in the paddy itself.

4. A Comparison of Methods

It will be instructive to draw comparisons between the above methods. The Chinese Yu Tang fish pond system requires quite a bit of labor in that it involves digging out the field, building up the surrounding area, and providing the fish with food. It is a bit labor intensive.

i. The Chinese Yu Tang Fish Pond System (from Chugoku Nogyo no Dento to Gendai - The Traditional and Modern in Chinese Agriculture, (Nobunkyo Publishing).

"One makes foundations by digging up mud from a lowland, or wetland, area and piling it around the circumference. One then converts the excavated area into a pond and the dumping area as a foundation for a dry field. Sixty percent of that area is dry foundation and 40% is pond. Plant mulberries in the dry portion and raise fish in the pond portion. The mulberry leaves

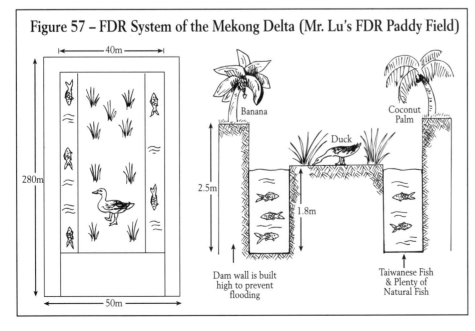

Figure 57 – FDR System of the Mekong Delta (Mr. Lu's FDR Paddy Field)

The methods used by Mr. Lu and in Fujian Province, China for the Azolla, Rice, Fish System described above need less day to day care, but also require the digging of a pond around the rice paddies. This requires a great deal of labor. Furthermore, there is some resistance to sacrificing important land for rice production solely for the purpose of these ponds.

In comparison to these models, I think that my Integrated Rice, Azolla, Duck and Fish Farming, which uses the paddy itself as a pond, is comparatively labor efficient. On the other hand, since my method does not involve digging an especially deep pond, it can only accommodate relatively smaller fish. Nonetheless each of these methods is remarkably well adapted to local natural features.

5. The Curious Natural Traits of Loaches

What kind of fish could be best raised in the duck rice paddies in your country? Tilapia, carp, or perhaps grass carp? I am keeping loaches in my rice paddies because these fish have a number of characteristics which make them particularly suitable for integrated rice and duck farming.

i. Paddy fields as a native home
Since ancient times loaches have inhabited rice fields and waterways in Japan. This is a most important point. The water temperature in relatively shallow paddies rises quickly, promoting the generation of food as well as soft, protective mud. Unlike crucians and carp, loaches are small even when fully grown, allowing them to live comfortably in paddy fields. Even so, they get bigger in a surprisingly short period of time when raised in this manner because the microbes, water fleas, *Orthocladius akamusi* and tubificid worms provide a continual abundance of food.

ii. Living even without water
Loaches can breath through their gills and also through their bowels. For this reason they can dive under the mud and live even when the water level is very low. This is to say that their water requirements and limitations are not as strict as for other fish. In this sense, they resemble the ducks, which are also amphibious, sturdy and resilient creatures. Loaches have a strong will to live and can even survive in a bucket for several days without food.

6. Considering mutual action

i. Food
In an integrated rice, azolla, duck paddy field, the ducks eat the azolla and their droppings become nourishment,

propagating a surprising number of aquatic plants and animals. These water fleas, tubificid worms, midge larvae, plankton, etc., become food for the fish, allowing them to quickly grow large within the pond even without additional food.

Artificially spawned young loaches 3 to 5 millimeters in length will grow to 10 centimeters in length and 6 to 8 millimeters in diameter after two to three months in a duck paddy field. You will also have a multitude of loaches if you breed their eggs in the pond. These facts testify to the quality of the environment created by a duck, fish integrated system.

ii. Protection from foreign invaders
What I have created through this integrated rice, azolla, duck and fish farming system is not merely a superior method to circulate material, but one having an extremely rational interactive mechanism. The ducks make the rice paddy muddy to the extent that beyond a certain water depth it is not possible to see the loaches on the bottom. Moreover, the azolla covers the muddy water like a thick mulch, making it even more difficult to see the loaches. I have almost never seen egrets, herons or other fish predators in my duck paddy fields. They must be under the impression that all of the ducks have already eaten any available food — either that or their pride does not allow them to dine together with the ducks. In this sense, the ducks act as "camouflage" ("kamo" means "duck" in Japanese) against egrets, herons, and other foreign invaders.

Figure 58 – Camouflage

I won't enter a paddy field with ducks!

Egrets, Night Herons

Rice Plants

I can't see anything because of the Azolla's mulch & muddy water!

Azolla Mulch

Duck

Loaches

7. Integrated Rice, Azolla, Duck, Fish farming in practice

i. Two methods of cultivation

There are two ways to cultivate fish in rice paddies. One is to stock the pond with artificially hatched young fish. The other is to stock the pond with adult fish and then let them spawn naturally.

a. Stocking young fish

I stock the paddy field with baby loaches which have been hatched and raised in a water tank for one or two weeks, just prior to rice-planting. At that time they are from 3 mm to 5 mm long. Following the planting, I flood the field and release the fish. Though they are still small, they swim happily around the pond. They are small enough not to be discovered by egrets and herons. In my fields, the fish save themselves by hiding from their enemies in the muddiness caused by the ducks and under the azolla mulch. Because they get big so quickly, I release them in the pond as soon as possible.

b. Stocking adult fish

This is the method of stocking mature fish and letting them spawn naturally. Two-year-old fish are used. This method does not require much labor or hassle.

ii. Cultivation management in practice

This method, which I developed for Japanese paddy fields with their concrete drains and irrigation ditches, may not be suited to the circumstances in other Asian countries. So I will just briefly explain the main points.

a. Methods to Prevent Escape

Loaches are renowned escape artists, able to get away through the smallest holes. However, I make my levees just a little higher than others and always use embankment sheets to prevent water leakage. To prevent the fish from escaping, I cover the water inlet and drainage openings with nets (see Figure 59b).

Loaches can easily escape through water inlet openings. For this reason I firmly fasten nets (the plastic type used for onion bags in Japan) to the mouth of the pipe. However, garbage, grass and other articles can get stuck in the net and cause clogging, so every morning I inspect it when I come to feed the ducks.

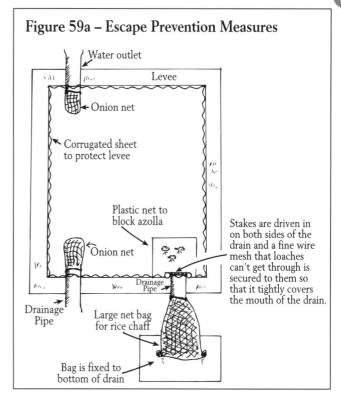

Figure 59a – Escape Prevention Measures

Water outlet
Levee
Onion net
Corrugated sheet to protect levee
Plastic net to block azolla
Onion net
Drainage Pipe
Drainage Pipe
Large net bag for rice chaff
Bag is fixed to bottom of drain
Stakes are driven in on both sides of the drain and a fine wire mesh that loaches can't get through is secured to them so that it tightly covers the mouth of the drain.

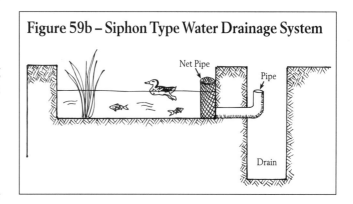

Figure 59b – Siphon Type Water Drainage System

Net Pipe
Pipe
Drain

As shown in Figure 59a, I make an enclosure around the drainage openings with nets to prevent the azolla from being washed away. Next, I place a fine metal net over the mouth of the drain to prevent the loaches from escaping. In addition, I bind bag-shaped netting to the pipes sticking out into the drainage ditches and fasten this to the bottom of the ditches. In heavy rains when the water rises, loaches caught in the net will be killed by friction from the net and the falling water if the net is left hanging in mid-air. If you attach the net to the bottom of the ditch, the bottom of the net will be washed downstream by the current so the loaches are not hit by the falling water.

b. Water Management

In principle, a deep water level should be maintained in rice paddies containing loaches. If the water level is kept too shallow, the loaches will become visible to ducks and other predators and become easy prey. If the paddy is temporarily drained, one must be sure to first move out the ducks. Anyway, the paddy is generally not drained at this stage in Integrated Duck and Rice Farming.

c. Catching Loaches during Drainage

The ducks are taken out of the field when the rice comes into ear. This is when I start draining the water. The first time I drain the field, only a few of the loaches get caught in the nets. This is because a number of them are holed up under the mud. What do we do when this happens?

First, dry out the field for one to two days. Then flood the field with a generous amount of water and redrain it. This time a great number of the loaches will be in the nets. Doing this apparently puts them into a "Get me out of here!" state of mind. Repeating the draining, refilling procedure for two or three weeks allows you to catch a lot of the fish.

d. Catching Loaches prior to Drainage

There are ways to catch the loaches before draining the paddy field. After releasing loaches in the paddy field, give them feed every evening at the same time and place. In Japan, commercial feed consisting of fish dung mixed with starch can be bought. Wild mud snails can also be crushed and given as feed. If fed each evening this way, the loaches will form a strong habit to eat every evening. Now it is simple - when you want to catch them, just put feed in a trap and sink it in the same place at the same time. Just as with the ducks, feeding is a good way to communicate with the loaches.

This is my Integrated Duck Rice, Azolla, Fish Farming system. Now you try your own version of this system in your country. I think that you will find it to be the best overall.

III. A New Technique - Bird Tillage

Allowing Ducks into the Paddy Field before Rice Seedling Transplantation.

1. What is Bird Tillage?

The Yue people of China apparently have a word for "bird tillage" (Chinese: niaogeng). Prof. Naokazu Kokubun of Baiko Women's University has written, "Birds which gather in the paddy fields looking for food happen to perform the function of intertillage, and their excreta also become fertilizer. This is probably the reason why the words "bird tillage" and "bird field" (Chinese: niaotian) still remain in the language of the Yue people."

Ducks perform a wide variety of activities in the paddy fields. The overall effect for rice cultivation is aptly expressed by the term "bird tillage."

Perhaps you have water buffalo in your country. I have heard that there has been from ancient times an interesting technique used in Southeast Asia known as "hoof tillage." "Hoof" in this case refers to the hooves of cattle and horses.

"About a month before the seedling transplantation period, water buffaloes are driven into marshy ground overgrown with kayatsurigusa [a kind of galingale common as a weed in Japanese paddy fields] (Cyperus Microiria). ...In this way, the water buffalo herd walks around and around the whole field until the luxuriant grass is trampled into the mud." (Yoshikazu Takaya, How to Understand Rice[in Japanese], NHK Books)

I wonder if you use "hoof tillage" in your country. If you replace the hoof with the webfoot of the duck, you will get a general sense of what "bird tillage" is all about.

I know from experience that if you allow water into the paddy field in the winter and then place ducks or carp in the field, the following summer there will be hardly any weeds at all in the field.

I have also heard from farmers near Ho Chi Minh in Vietnam that they drive parent (adult) ducks into the paddy fields before rice plant transplantation so that they will trample down the weeds.

In other words, the diverse activity of ducks in the paddy field amounts to "bird tillage." It is also possible to say that a "wider interpretation of bird tillage" would include allowing ducks into the paddy field after rice seedling transplantation, as in integrated rice and duck farming. However, for convenience I will define the term "bird tillage" as used here as the use of ducks in

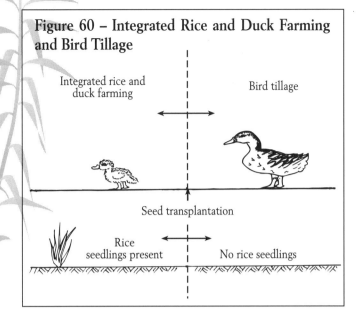

Figure 60 – Integrated Rice and Duck Farming and Bird Tillage

Integrated rice and duck farming

Bird tillage

Seed transplantation

Rice seedlings present

No rice seedlings

Figure 61– The Four Bird Tillage Methods

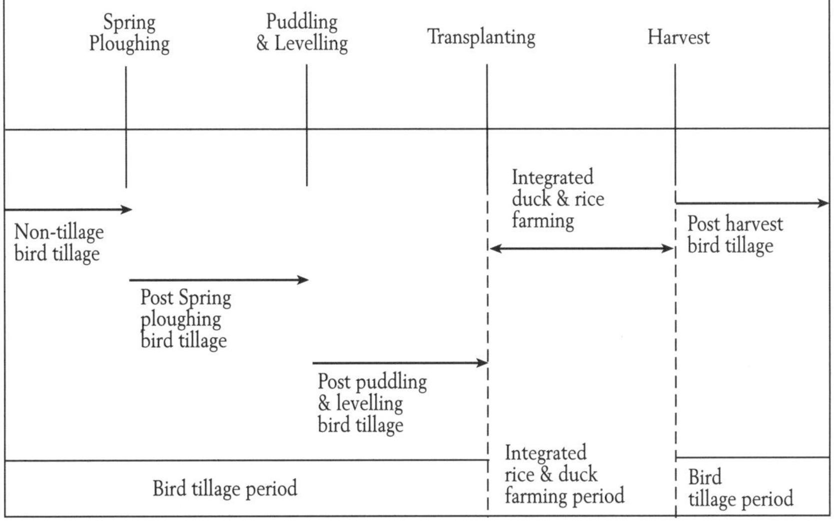

Spring Ploughing	Puddling & Levelling	Transplanting	Harvest

Non-tillage bird tillage

Post Spring ploughing bird tillage

Post puddling & levelling bird tillage

Integrated duck & rice farming

Post harvest bird tillage

Bird tillage period

Integrated rice & duck farming period

Bird tillage period

Bird tillage has helped me to develop this idea as it enables the use of ducks in the paddy field before seedling transplantation.

In the case of Japanese seedling transplantation rice cultivation, bird tillage can be divided into four categories; post-harvest bird tillage, non-tillage bird tillage, post-spring ploughing bird tillage, and post-puddling and leveling bird tillage (Figure 61). Duck activity in a dry paddy field is included in bird tillage, but here I am assuming the much more effective method of bird tillage, that with water in the paddy field.

i.   Post-Harvest Bird Tillage

Post-harvest bird tillage is a method for using ducks in a paddy field into which water has been introduced following completion of the fall harvest. Because gleanings (missed ears of rice), barnyard millet and weed seeds are eaten by the ducks, or are trampled into the mud, the appearance of weeds the following spring and summer is greatly suppressed. At the same time, the duck excreta are also quite effective as nutrient (basal dressing) for the rice plants.

ii.   Non-Tillage Bird Tillage

Non-tillage bird tillage is a method by which water is introduced into a paddy field in which Chinese milk vetch and weeds are growing approximately one to two months before rice seedling transplantation. Then, instead of ploughing (leveling) with a tractor, ducks are allowed into the paddy field.

If you actually try flooding a field of Chinese milk vetch and then letting the ducks graze in the field, they will stick their necks into the c.m.vetch and literally gorge themselves on it. Compared to when the field is ploughed, duck feed is far more plentiful in the unploughed field, and the water makes it easier for the ducks to eat.

Depending on how you look at it, ploughing takes the grasses, seeds, and insects that would make good feed for the ducks and "wastes" it by burying it under the mud.

the paddy field before seedling transplantation has been carried out, or after harvest.

As shown in Figure 60, I shall define specifically "bird tillage" as allowing ducks into the paddy field when there are no rice plants planted, and "integrated rice and duck farming" as allowing ducks into a paddy field which has been planted with rice.

2. The Four Bird Tillage Methods

Up to now, I have said that the key to integrated rice and duck farming is to introduce ducks into the paddy field as soon as possible after the transplantation of rice seedlings. Because of this I have tried to use large and healthy seedlings with small duck chicks.

Looked at from the point of view of the effective use of duck feed, non-tillage bird tillage is a very interesting technique. With bird tillage, even the largest ducks can be allowed into the field, since there is no rice growing there. When bird tillage is carried out with large ducks the mud (soil) is well stirred and the weed seeds on the surface of the soil are either eaten or pushed well into the mud. This results in suppression of early weed appearance.

Following non-tillage bird tillage it is possible to transplant rice seedlings directly into the field without ploughing. It is also possible to carry out direct sowing of rice without tillage. A crucial point is that the paddy field must always be kept flooded. If the field is dried out, then even after bird tillage weeds will appear from deep in the ground since oxygen is now being supplied to the soil.

iii. Post-Spring Ploughing Bird Tillage
This is a bird tillage technique whereby ducks are allowed into a paddy field after spring ploughing has been carried out, but into which water has been introduced and with no puddling and leveling. Bird tillage by the ducks performs the task of puddling and leveling, and the water holding ability of the paddy field improves after about two weeks or so. It is then possible to transplant rice seedlings or carry out direct sowing into the field.

iv. Post-Puddling and Leveling Bird Tillage
In this technique, large ducks are allowed into the paddy field immediately after puddling and leveling, which is carried out about one to three weeks before the transplantation of rice seedlings. This helps to suppress the appearance of weeds for a while after seedling transplantation, and also greatly reduces the number of weeds when they do eventually appear. In addition, the large number of insects that appear during puddling and leveling become feed for the ducks.

It is possible to apply this technique to paddy fields which are affected by an abundance of barnyard millet, or where rice cultivation by direct sowing is to be carried out.

In the case of direct sowing into a flooded paddy field, ducks cannot be allowed into the field until the seedlings reach a suitable size. Weeds can appear and grow large during this time, but this problem can be avoided by suppressing the growth of early weeds through the use of bird tillage. When the rice plants reach a suitable size, small ducks can then be allowed to graze in the field. This technique may be effective in areas of Asia where direct sowing of rice is carried out.

3. The Effects of Bird Tillage

From the above, we can see that bird tillage has several different advantages from integrated rice and duck farming when looked at from the perspectives of both rice cultivation and animal raising (stockbreeding). These can be summarized as follows:

i. Large weeds which grow in the paddy field before seedling transplantation are pushed directly under the muddy water in the field, thereby eliminating and suppressing weeds,
ii. By carrying out bird tillage in paddy fields before seedling transplantation, the appearance of weeds after transplantation is suppressed and postponed,
iii. Indigenous insect pests in the paddy field before seedling transplantation are suppressed (or eliminated),
iv. Duck excreta from the bird tillage period act as a basal dressing, and thus has a good nutrient supply effect,
v. Weeds and insect pests present in the bird tillage period become good duck feed,
vi. Bird tillage also is effective in preventing water leakage.

4. How Weed suppression and elimination works with Non-Tillage Bird Tillage

A non-tillage bird tillage paddy field will have a large number of tall weeds growing in it before bird tillage is started. If water is allowed into the paddy field at this stage, this is enough to cause land (upland?) grasses such as Chinese milk vetch and karasunoendou (*Vicia angustifolia*) to wither and die. However, suzumenoteppou (*Alopecurus aequalis var. amurensis*), American sloughgrass (kazunokogusa, *Beckmannia syzigachne)*, and barnyard millet will not be affected much by the water.

When ducks are allowed to carry out bird tillage, however, all of the weeds (grasses) are pushed over and trampled by the ducks. Even the biggest weeds (grasses) will die quickly when completely submerged in the muddy water.

This "complete submergence in the muddy water" is the key factor in weed suppression and elimination in non-tillage bird tillage.

IV. A New Technique: Deep Flooding + Quick Drainage + Medium-sized Ducks

We have nearly reached the end of this book now, but lastly I want to write about a practical technique for the suppression and elimination of weeds, especially barnyard millet.

1. Barnyard Millet in Deep Water

Every spring, in March and April, I sow barnyard millet in several pots in a vinyl greenhouse. I vary the depth of the water and carry out germination and growth observations on the barnyard millet. At the same time I also carry out investigations with the same depth of muddy water.

The results are quite clear. Generally, the deeper the water the lower will be the germination and growth rate of the barnyard millet. Using soil from my own paddy fields, I found that barnyard millet will not appear if the water is more than 13 cm deep. This is probably because when the water is deep, reduction occurs and there is not enough oxygen for germination to take place.

Naturally, for the same depth of water, germination and growth of weeds becomes greatly suppressed in muddy water.

In fact, the depth of water in my own paddy fields is only about 5 to 10 cm. If I adjust the water to be at the top end of that range, even if the barnyard millet does germinate the leaves will be pale and the plants will be thin and spindly.

If you scoop up one of these barnyard millet plants with the roots intact, you will find

that it will not be able to support itself without water and will flop down flat on the mud.

The roots of the barnyard millet will be quite different depending on the depth of the water. Barnyard millet which has grown in shallow water will be firm and strong above ground and will have a strong root structure.

On the other hand, millet which has grown in deep water will be thin and spindly above ground and will have a very poor and weak root structure below ground.

However, when the tips of the leaves of the barnyard millet appear above the surface of the water, even deep water will lose its growth suppression effect.

Thus the effect of deep water on the growth of weeds (barnyard millet) is valid only before they appear or in the very early stages when the tips of the leaves do not emerge above the surface of the water.

One plant, duck tongue weed (*Monochoria vaginalis var. plantaginea* [an improved variety of this is apparently eaten as a vegetable in some parts of southeast Asia.]), will appear even in 10 cm of water. But then duck tongue weed is one of the ducks' favorite foods!

2. Practical applications of deep water

As mentioned above, bird tillage is an effective anti-weed (barnyard millet) technique. In practice, however, there may be paddy fields where bird tillage is impossible because water management practices make it impossible to flood a field at an early period.

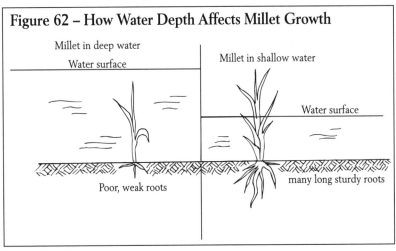

Figure 62 – How Water Depth Affects Millet Growth

Millet in deep water
Water surface

Millet in shallow water
Water surface

Poor, weak roots

many long sturdy roots

Millet grown in deep water has weak roots.

V. Some New Thoughts on Integrated Farming - Fascinating Integrated Rice, Duck, Azolla and Fish Farming

"Are paddy fields only for growing rice?" ask the ducks in the paddy field. This is a question on the basics of agriculture, highlighting the perspective of "integrated farming."

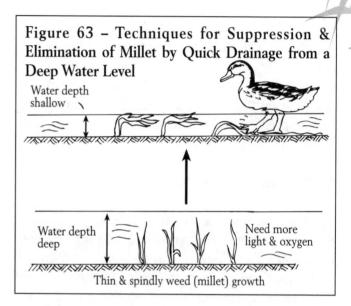

Figure 63 – Techniques for Suppression & Elimination of Millet by Quick Drainage from a Deep Water Level

Water depth shallow

Water depth deep

Need more light & oxygen

Thin & spindly weed (millet) growth

There are also many cases where it is not possible to allow the ducks to graze within two weeks after seedling transplantation.

What can be done in these cases?

While observing the weed suppression and elimination mechanism of non-tillage bird tillage, i.e. complete submergence below muddy water, I had the following idea: "Why not just make it easy for the barnyard millet already growing to flop over?" If the barnyard millet is submerged beneath the muddy water it will die.

Keeping the water level as high as possible in the field for over three weeks, allow thin and spindly barnyard millet to appear. Then quickly drain the paddy field to a shallow level of water. The weak, thin and spindly millet will now flop over and float on the surface.

Three to four-week-old medium-sized ducks are then allowed into the field to graze. The thin and weak millet will now be trampled by the ducks and will be nicely buried in the mud.

If the ducks are allowed into the paddy field while the water is still deep, the millet will be standing straight up in the water and not easily trampled down by the ducks' feet.

In order to arrange for a good deep level of water in the paddy field, it is important first to ensure that good, strong rice seedlings are planted. In your country you may be planting large seedlings by hand, and so you will probably find it quite easy to use this technique.

In agricultural modernization so far, it has been assumed that "the paddy field is a place to grow just one plant, namely rice." However, our friends the ducks brought the possibility of simultaneously growing rice and livestock in the same space. So the paddy field has become a place for rice farming as well as stockbreeding. The ducks have given us a new perspective about the paddy field.

In 1993, I first learned about the nitrogen-fixing water plant azolla from Mr. Iwao Watanabe, who was then a professor at Mie University. Since 1994, I have been engrossed in practical research on integrated rice, duck and azolla farming. Since 1996, I have added fish (carp and loaches) , and have enjoyed experimenting with integrated rice, duck, azolla and fish farming. These methods developed organically from the basic principles of integrated farming.

It is said that a food crisis awaits us in the twenty first century. The times call upon each nation in Asia to increase its food production and self-sufficiency as much as possible making best use of the limited available farmland. Since a further increase in the area under cultivation is no longer feasible, there are three ways to achieve this:

1. Increase the productivity of each crop/output, such as rice, wheat, livestock, etc. (the conventional method)
2. Increase the overall productivity of limited farmland by growing different crops by rotation in a given sequence (crop rotation).
3. Produce two or more crops/outputs (crops, livestock, fish, etc.) at once in the same farmland (integrated farming/mixed cropping).

Method 1 is that which has been pursued in agricultural modernization. It is an important method which should continue to be pursued.

Method 2 is that of traditional farming in Asia. It calls for careful management, and usually also requires many kinds of farm work and major inputs of labor.

The methods of mixed cropping and of integrated farming in Method 3 are similar. Mixed cropping tends to mean combining different crops with each other, and is widely practiced in traditional Asian farming. It also requires massive labor inputs. In normal mixed cropping, there can only be limited use of weeding machines, and harvesting must be done by hand.

However, integrated farming includes combinations of plants and animals, such as crops, livestock and fish. As shown in Figure 55 above, there is an organic functional relationship between them. Though crop rotation and mixed cropping require massive inputs of often complicated human labor to control weeds and insects and supply nutrients to the soil, these functions are performed naturally within the integrated farming system (by the azolla, ducks, fish, etc.). Integrated farming is a resource and labor-saving technique.

I believe there are exciting possibilities for organically combining crop rotation and integrated farming from a contemporary perspective, as shown in Figure 64, and that such approaches will play an important role in agriculture in the 21st Century.

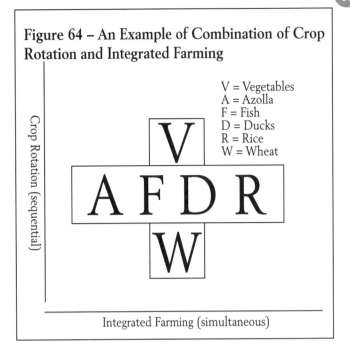

Figure 64 – An Example of Combination of Crop Rotation and Integrated Farming

Crop Rotation (sequential)

V A F D R W

V = Vegetables
A = Azolla
F = Fish
D = Ducks
R = Rice
W = Wheat

Integrated Farming (simultaneous)

VI. Integrated Rice and Duck Farming in 1998 - The Ducks did a Splendid Job Controlling Pests

Perhaps due to early season high temperatures from abnormal weather, we were visited by a lot of insects in 1998. For the first time in several years, we saw paddy fields with hopperburn due to brown rice plant hoppers or with leaves turned white by rice leafhoppers. It was a year that the ducks' overall power, especially in controlling insect pests, really stood out.

"There ain't no plant hopper damage in them duck paddies, but plant hoppers really blighted my field, which I weeded with golden snails. I only got three bales. Yup, duck paddies are the best." A number of people commented this way. The ducks have earned a good name for themselves.

Mr. Suenobu of the Extension Centre and I did another investigation of insect pests in 1998. The number of insect pests and spiders about two weeks after taking the ducks out of the paddy field was as shown in Table 24 below.

The number of brown rice plant hopper (*Nilaparvata lugens*) larvae in the duck plot was surprisingly low: one fifth of that of the control plot and one half of that of the nearby conventional plots, which had been

Table 24 – Insect Pests and Spiders in the Duck Plot, Control Plot and Conventional Plot (investigated 14 September 1998)

	Sogatella furcifera adult	Sogatella furcifera larvae	Nilaparvata lugens adult	Nilaparvata lugens larvae	Nephottix apicalis larvae	Laodelphax striatellus larvae	spiders
Duck Plot	0	4	6	23	9	3	46
Control Plot	0	0	86	108	12	0	28
Conventional plot*	2	2	8	43	0	2	19

* The pesticides Admire (a fungicide/insecticide applied to seedling bed) and Kasbracide (mid August) were used in the conventional plot.

sprayed with the pesticides Admire and Kasbracide. On the other hand, it had quite a few spiders: twice as many as in the control plot and 2.5 times as many as in the conventional plots. The number of spiders in the control plot was less than in the duck plot, not because we miscounted, but because the spiders were scattered among the weeds growing in the control plot.

As far as this table shows, it seems that the ducks' pest control effect considerably exceeds that of a combination of Admire and Kasbracide. By the way, there was a major outbreak of rice leaf rollers (Cnaphalocrecis medinalis) in the conventional plots that we investigated, though the figures are not shown in the Table.

Seeing the good job that the ducks did for us again this year, I was overjoyed as well as reminded of earlier days. Prior to encountering Aigamo ducks, I had been growing organic rice without using any agrichemicals for ten years. I had to pick the weeds by hand. Every three or four years, our paddy fields suffered hopperburn due to plant hoppers. Watching the plant hoppers wipe out the still unripened rice plants in a matter of one night, I used to feel so bitter and anxious that I could not sleep.

In the eleven years since I met with the Aigamo duck, I have so far not had any such worries.

It is usually said that spiders and other omnivorous pest predators are important for controlling damage from plant hoppers and other insect pests. This is common knowledge written in just about any book on insect pests.

However, in the agricultural ecosystem of the duck paddy field, the duck plays an even more remarkable role than spiders as an "omnivorous super pest predator." Furthermore, we humans can eat the ducks, so they not only control the insects, but convert them into food as well.

Appendix 1

Latin names of plants mentioned in the text

Common Name	Latin Name/s
American sloughgrass	*Kazunokogusa, Beckmannia syzigachne*
American Sloughgrass	*Beckmannia syzigachne*
Azolla	*Azolla filiculoides, A. pinnata, A. microphylla, A. caroliniana, A. mexicana, A. rubra, A. nilotica*
Azolla's algae	*Anabaena azollae*
Azolla combination	*A. filiculoides, x A. microphylla plus Ooakaukigusa A. Hybrid 4087 Japonica*
Barnyard grass (millet)	*"Hie" Echinochloa frumentacea or a combination of any of the below:*
Inubie	*Echinochloa crus-galli Beauv.*
Tainubie	*Echinochloa crus-galli Beauv. var. oryzicola Ohwi*
Himetainubie	*Echinochloa crus-galli Beauv. var. formosensis Ohwi*
Chinese milk vetch (renge)	*Astralagus sinicus L.*
Distel chum knot grass	*Paspalum*
Duck tongue weed	*Lindernia procumbens*
Green floating grass	*Spirodela polyrhiza*
Green floating grass	*Lemna paucicostata*
Karasunoendou	*Vicia angustifulia*
Kishusnzameno - hie	
Konagi	*Monochoria vaginalis*
Mizugayaisuti	
Mulberry	*Morus alba*
Rarasunoendou	*Vicia angustifolia*
Smallflower umbrella plant	*Cyperus difformis L.*
Suzumenoteppou	*Alopecurus æqualis*
Umbrella plant	*Cyperus serotinas*
Weed sedge	*Cyperus microiria*

Appendix 2

Retaining a family farm; food security, and farm income
by Bill Mollison

A cursory search of Western machinery catalogues, or machinery sales, will quickly convince you that every sort of large machine for the cultivation of crops, and the harvest of that crop is for sale. It is as apparent that any crop processing machines are "not for sale", nor are any small cultivators or harvesters.

The small or family farm has been the backbone of food supply for thousands of years. By large firms controlling processing, such farms became uneconomic, and we hear the call to "get big or get out", now changed to "get big and crash big".

In a recent visit to Japan, we find very small family farms (1-5 Ha) doing very well. A farmer with $1\frac{1}{2}$ ha of vegetable crop and $1\frac{1}{2}$ ha of rice can own two vehicles, travel around, and support a large family. There are two main aids to such affluence:

1) Selling direct to consumers (60-120 households per farm), now the primary market system in Japan,

2) Processing on farm.

A small farmers' barn is often full of small (ride on) crop machines, to enable very small fields to be used. For every one of these, there are 5 or more processing machines (for example, huskers, dryers, seed cleaners, bagging equipment, packaging systems, ferment vats, rice polishers, separaters, feed mills, small timber milling equipment, incubators for poultry etc. etc. etc.). Thus, in Japan most processing can take place on the farm, including the making of miso and pickles, and their packaging of polished rice, rice bran and vegetables.

Thus farmers can supply a retail market, carried in tiny trucks to consumers houses, farmers describe their consumers as "family". On the farm, all crop wastes immediately return to livestock as feed, then to the fields. Consumers pay for, and demand organic food (meat or vegetables) and pay well for it. Delivering vegetables, rice, root crop, greens, eggs and some fruit a small farmer delivers (per week) 33-50 US$ of product to each of 100 houses and makes $US3,300 to 5,000 per week. This is often the *annual* income of Western farmers!

I believe that such systems are essential for a healthy rural economy, and I would see the key to such success as small, and clever, processing systems suited to a wide variety of products. Even the tofu factories are no larger than a single car garage!

*A*fterword

I attend a zazen (seated meditation) meeting at a nearby Buddhist temple twice a month. As I am sitting quietly, various thoughts and feelings well up in my mind, much like clouds floating up into the sky.

We often say that we "think so and so" or "feel so and so," as though we are the ones "doing the thinking." However, the truth is that "thoughts" and "feelings" arise spontaneously in our minds from somewhere.

I did not write this book, so much as I merely put together and flavoured the thoughts that spontaneously floated up in my mind, and the various things taught to me by the people of Asia and by the rice plants and ducks in the paddy field.

In May, 1992, the ducks led me to Guilin City, China. Dr. Zhang, a researcher of waterfowl, presented me with a hanging scroll inscribed with the words "Thousand Miles - One Wind." I took it as an eye-opening invitation to jointly study Integrated Rice and Duck Farming from the broad perspective of agriculture in Asia.

In China, there is the beautiful expression "my native village, abundant in fish and rice." It describes the beautiful scenery of rural Asia with its rich nature and paddy fields, rivers and ponds yielding much rice and fish. It is my wish that your villages will forever and ever remain beautiful as "villages abundant in fish, rice and ducks!"

In Japan, there has been an ethos that the paddy fields, farmland and mountains are not anyone's "private property," but that they are on loan to us from our ancestors. If we take this stance, it is our responsibility to pass on the paddy fields, farmlands and mountains to our children and grandchildren in the same beautiful state as when we first received them from our ancestors. The same goes for our planet Earth. I will be happy if Integrated Rice and Duck Farming can contribute even slightly to making this happen.

I am looking forward to your "duck mail." If there is the opportunity, I will get on my magical duck and come flying to your village. As fellow farmers, let's share many things. I am certain that such sharing is the key to development of Integrated Rice and Duck Farming.

It was only through the support of many people with whom I have had the good fortune to meet, that an ordinary farmer such as myself, with little knowledge or talent, could have brought this book to publication. I would like to express my heartfelt gratitude to Bill and Lisa Mollison for providing the opportunity to write this book and even giving a wonderful title for it, to Tony Boys, Puck Brecher and Tom Eskildsen for devoting much valuable time to translate, edit and correct my poorly written drafts, to Tomoko Moriya for drawing the cheerful illustrations, to Soichi Iwaki for helping with layout, to Shodo Munakata for his editorial supervision, to Akiko Suzuki (formerly with JVC) for advice regarding names of people and places in Vietnam, to Mr. Iwao Watanabe (retired professor of Mie University) for advice regarding agricultural/technical terms, and to our many friends in Asia. I am indebted to all of you. I thank you very much from my heart.

Gassho (with hands joined)

May 1, 1999
Takao Furuno,
Farmer
824 Jumyo, Keisen-cho, Kaho-gun,
Fukuoka-ken, Japan 820-0603
Tel/Fax: 0948-65-2018

"I am flying to Asia!"

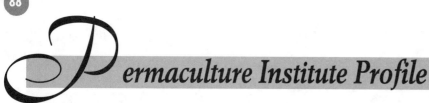

Permaculture Institute Profile

Mission Statement

Promotion of sustainable system design known as Permaculture, through education, publishing, translation, implementation, the development of curricula, and the establishment and administration of aid projects.

Origins

The Permaculture Institute is a non-profit educational trust. Founded in 1978 by Dr. Bill Mollison, it was based in Stanley Tasmania for ten years. In 1988 the Institute moved to the sub tropics of Northern N.S.W. returning to Tasmania in 1998.

Functions

The Institute's primary focus is education, with emphasis on producing indigenous teachers. Thus, the skills gained spread exponentially with the Permaculture global movement, the transfer of information is immeasurable. There are no boundaries or limitations governing the extent of influence of Permaculture practices. The Institute targets international exposure, with particular emphasis on producing teachers, and the general populace of developing countries and communities in need.

Permaculture Defined

Taken from the Latin Permanens - to endure or persist through time and cultura - cultures; meaning permanent cultures. Permaculture is an interdisciplinary design science, focussed on sustainable system design. As stated by Dr. Mollison in 1978, "Sustainable is defined as a system, which over its lifetime produces energy equivalent to or in excess of what it consumes.

A Dynamic Process

We live on a planet in crisis. Often individuals feel powerless to effect change. Permaculture offers positive solutions to the problems facing the world, using ecology for the basis of study, design and implementation which produces enduring, functional, sustainable and integrated systems that support human settlements and natural ecosystems.

Permaculture design includes but is not limited to the principles and practices of sustainable development of soil, water, crop, forest, architectural, business and financial systems, domestic food and water security, community development and micro-banking. By understanding Permaculture one can create a self-sustaining environment in any situation, whether it be a large tract of land or a small urban setting.

Following Permaculture design principles, the placement of system components is determined by the needs of each component and the use of its produce. For the system to be sustainable all components must provide or conserve sufficient energy over their life span to build and maintain themselves as well as produce excess yield which can be returned to the system.

In a nutshell, Permaculture is the science of best relative placement of components in a plan or pattern, in order to increase resources, conserve or create energy and to reduce or eliminate pollution or waste. It is an information rich, interdisciplinary study crossing all boundaries, enabled by the bridging of ancient wisdom and new technology. By embracing new information and technological advancement, Permaculture advances as a dynamic process.

Permaculture ethics

Permaculture operates on three ethics: 1. Care of the Earth, 2. Care of Species, 3. Return of Excess to the First Two. Courses are given from an introductory level to the 72-hour Permaculture Design Certificate Course.

Permaculture Network

The Permaculture network is truly global; groups, associations and organisations that work with Permaculture design principles currently number over 450. Permaculture Global Directory, Permaculture International Journal, 1999.

Constituency Served

Since the founding of this Institute, Permaculture Institutes have flourished worldwide in Europe, North and South America, Asia, Africa, Middle East, Pacific Island countries and Australia, as independent, yet often, interconnected bases for local Permaculture teaching and projects. The constituency is truly global; wherever we have an impact on the environment, there is a need for sustainable system design and sustainable environmental practices.

Founder and Executive Director of the Permaculture Institute

Dr. Bill Mollison, is a researcher, author, scientist, naturalist, and founder of Permaculture. Dr. Mollison's work is translated into 26 languages. He has received numerous major awards including,

1981 The Right Livelihood Award, - Sweden known as the alternative Nobel Prize.
1989 Honorary Fellow of the Schumacher Society- England
1991 Russian Academy of Agricultural Science Member - first foreigner
1991 Vavilov Medal- Russia for contributions to sustainable agricultural & community systems
1993 Outstanding Australian Achiever - National Australia Day Council
1993 Banksia Environmental Award - WA Australia
1996 Steward of Sustainable Agriculture - Asilomar, CA USA
1999 Australian Icon - one of 45

Other Directors

Lisa Mollison has been a Director since January 1997. Lisa was raised on a California rice farm owned by her family for five generations. She worked for over a decade in commercial agriculture. In 1991, Lisa set out to promote sustainable agriculture on a personal scale and founded the business, Foodscapes Organic. During five years of operation Foodscapes installed over 300 back yard mini farms. She is experienced in business management, surveying, soil analysis, broad-scale small grain production, licensed landscape contracting and publishing.

Funding

Over the years, Mollison taught and worked in the USA and Europe; this paid expenses to teach courses and set up projects in Third World countries. Additionally, all profit from the publishing arm of the Institute, Tagari Publications is transferred to the Institute annually. No government or non-government organisation has funded the Institute's work to date. The present directors are self funded volunteers, who donate their time overseeing the Institute's operations.

Summary

Over 4,000 Permaculture projects operate independently around the world today. Permaculture grows exponentially as Permaculture teachers produce more Permaculture teachers. After personally planting the seeds of Permaculture in 120 countries, true to Mollison's vision, Permaculture is a part of every day life for millions.

"Our own personal efforts to effect change may seem insignificant to us but when our actions are combined with the actions of others who are also working towards a more sustainable and healthy world this is in effect a significant movement toward sustainability."

Bill Mollison

To learn more about Permaculture check out www.tagari.com

Tagari Publications Profile

Publishers for the Permaculture Institute since 1979

Mission
To publish and distribute the best in Permaculture research.

History
"Tagari" is a Tasmanian Aboriginal word meaning "those of us who are gathered here" or "us mob". Tagari began in 1978 as a community of people who worked and lived on eighty acres of swamp land in Stanley, Tasmania, researching and experimenting with Permaculture concepts. The development of sustainable design principles began here and together with the establishment of the Permaculture Institute, was the catalyst for the birth of the Permaculture ethic, which has since spread worldwide. Tagari Publications operates under the McAlistair Trading Trust set up in 1979, by Dr. Bill Mollison. The primary function of Tagari Publications is to help support the work of the Permaculture Institute by publishing and selling books about sustainability and then transferring profits to the Permaculture Institute at year's end. Please refer to the Permaculture Institute's Profile for details on the Institute's work. Since 1979 Tagari Publications has published 8 books and 8 booklets which are sold from its offices in NSW, and Tasmania, through book shops and 3 national and 4 international distributors.

Additionally, Tagari retails 80 titles, charts, posters, T-shirts, calendars and tools. Entry into e-commerce is currently being established.

Future books due out soon by Bill Mollison Include:
1. Traditional Food Processing
2. Sustainable Living in Cold Climates
3. Patterns and Designs in Nature
4. The Potato Papers: A Tasmanian Memoir
5. The Allium Alliance

Booklets published by Tagari:
The Oaks Booklet by John Fargher
Useful Bamboo Species Booklet by Andrew Jeeves
Useful Cactus, Agave and Aloe Species Booklet by Reny Mia Slay
Useful Climbing Plants Booklet by Bill Mollison
Useful Legume Species Booklet by John Fargher
Useful Onion Species Booklet by Bill Mollison
Useful Palms of the World Booklet by Bill Mollison
Useful Plants of the Wetlands Booklet by Bill Mollison

Authors Published by Tagari
The Power of Duck, Integrated Rice Duck Farming by Takao Furuno

Published Titles
Tagari currently publishes all of Dr. Mollison's books in English. They include:

Title	In Print
1. Permaculture One: A Perennial Agriculture for Human Settlements co-authored with David Holmgren	145,000
2. Permaculture Two: Practical Design for Town and Country	145,000
3. Permaculture: A Designer's Manual	150,000
4. Introduction to Permaculture	80,500
5. Ferment and Human Nutrition	11,600
6. Travels In Dreams, an autobiography	3,540
7. Foundation Year Book of the Permaculture Academy	6,000

The Permaculture Design Certificate Course and Resources

The Permaculture Design Certificate Course – 72 Hours

Permaculture is design science. The pragmatic approach of this work largely omits reference to those visions or beliefs classified as spiritual or mystical; not because these are not part of human experience, but because they are arrived at as a result of long contemplation or intense involvement with the mysteries that eternally surround us. We may dream understanding but it is something we cannot demand, define or teach to others; it is for each of us to develop. If we try to educate on the subject of design science we must omit belief.

Permaculture design utilises methods and strategies of design for nearly every conceivable situation, producing a predictable result, because of this, in theory and practice, it has universality. Like acccounting, Permaculture design utilises foundation rules, principles, strategies, education and terminology which are studied and applied worldwide.

Many courses are offered in Permaculture, but only one of them is eligible for a certificate in Permaculture Design. The certificate course is a standardised curriculum which includes all topics found in PERMACULTURE: A DESIGNERS' MANUAL, Mollison, Bill, 1988. This book is the foundation text and the curriculum for the certificate course as well as the definition of the scope of Permaculture. A teacher must give the entire curriculum, during the course. Material may not be omitted, however, teachers are encouraged to add relevant material from their own and local knowledge, and to utilise any teacher's aides they choose. Students need to ensure teachers are giving the full curriculum prior to enrolling with a teacher. As Permaculture laps the globe, many teachers are springing up and the best teachers produce the best teachers. Also, many people claim to have taught with Bill Mollison, or claim to have endorsement from Mollison. Students please note that such claims may be false and are encouraged to ensure the validity of the claim by contacting the Permaculture Institute at www.permaculture.org.au or www.tagari.com

Resources

There are five journals in English and most associations have a newsletter. The web is showing 8,000 Permaculture sites as of June, 2000. To streamline the resources listing we have listed the following. If you have trouble contacting anybody, give us a yell. We are happy to help.

Permaculture Global Directory – May 1999

A Contact list to hundreds of worldwide Permaculture projects, available from:
Permaculture International Journal
PO Box 6039, Lismore 2480, NSW, Australia
Ph: 61 2 6622 0020 Fax 61 2 6622 0579

American Permaculture Directory

A registry of American graduates and services available from:
Shade Tree Publishing 5515 N 7th Street Suite 5144, Phoenix, Arizona 85014, USA
Phone 1 602 279 3713 Fax 1 602 279 1874

Permaculture Books

Travels in Dreams *An Autobiography*

"What matters it, what went before or after, now with myself I shall begin and end" W. Shakespeare. Although the saga continues, the reader will get a good honest look at a man who has managed to cram many lifetimes into one, being reborn and starting life anew, armed with the knowledge gained from past endeavours. Bill has enchanted and transported groups the world over by mesmerizing and instructing them through his actions, words and song... *"What will you talk about?"* they ask, *"I don't know, but I will try to paint landscapes in their minds, throw pictures on the clouds of tomorrow's sky."* Bill Mollison.

Written in theme chapters, the reader can choose a theme to explore. The origins of Permaculture, in search of meaning, travels in the home country, stories of the bush, forests, working environments, coasts, islands, lakes, village and urban life, industry, institution, nostalgia, fantasies, travels of a Permaculture apostle, woo-woo worlds, sex and relationships, theories for all occasions and sprinkled throughout are heaps of Bill's poems both naughty and nice.

863 pages soft bound

"Interesting, rambling, spontaneous, funny..." Ari Clare Akermon, fisherman

"What will the world think of Australians if this sort of scurrilous rubbish becomes known?" Diocesan Newsletter, Melbourne

"I've not enjoyed a book so much in a very long time — it is sheer serendipity." John Bottoms, Bottoms English Lawyers

The Permaculture Book of Ferment and Human Nutrition

Emphasising the enhancement of nutrition, this is one of the most comprehensive books available today on the subject of storing and preserving foods. Recipes and processing methods have been collected from indigenous people worldwide. These practical and traditional techniques, many of which were nearly lost forever, have been collated and set out in a well-defined and easy to follow manual which is of value to anyone interested in processing and storing food.

"A truly fabulous book, a quirky gem, a classic. Mollison has written a comprehensive monograph on the international use of microbial fermentation in food and beverage production, from a cross-cultural, anthropological, and biological perspective." Dr. Marion Nestle, Dept. of Nutrition and Food Studies, New York University

288 pages soft bound

Permaculture Two

Practical Design for Town and Country in Permanent Agriculture

This book, which follows on from Permaculture One, is about design. It is a practical book dealing with the elements of design to create a sustainable system. Energy benefits are discussed relating to both domestic and broadacre environments.

"...Permaculture Two is about design, not gardening or livestock per se but as elements in a system intended to serve man, and the ends of good ecology... Good teachers have nothing to give but enthusiasm to learn; they cannot with the best will in the world, give their students knowledge. Thus it is 'how' to design, rather than designing your site which I am attempting here..." Bill Mollison

150 pages soft bound

Permaculture Books

Permaculture: A Designer's Manual

This is the definitive Permaculture design manual and has been in print since 1988. Written for teachers, students and designers, it follows on and greatly enlarges on the initial introductory texts, Permaculture One (1978) and Permaculture Two (1979) both of which are still in demand over twenty years after publication. Very little of the material found in this book is reproduced from the former texts. It covers all aspects of property design and natural farming techniques including:

- design methods
- understanding patterns in nature
- climatic factors
- water
- soils
- earthworks and their use in earth repair
- techniques and design strategies for both urban and rural applications
- the temperate climates
- dry lands
- cold climates
- humid cool climates
- humid tropics
- trees and their energy
- aquaculture
- waste management
- energy efficient architecture
- legal strategies and trusts
- effective working groups
- right livelihood
- money and finance
- ethical investment
- effective aid

580 pages hard bound

Introduction to Permaculture

Written to introduce readers to Permaculture concepts and design strategies - topics include: energy efficient site analysis, planning and design methods, house placement, design for temperate, dry-land and tropical regions, urban Permaculture garden layouts, land access and community funding systems, chicken and pig forage systems, orchards and home wood lots, how to influence micro-climate and a large section on selected plant species with climatic tolerances, heights and uses.

The book is set out as a step-by-step introduction to Permaculture with detailed instructions. Using simple language it describes the range of Permaculture for general consumption.

Very little content of Bill Mollison's other books are found within *Introduction to Permaculture*.

216 pages soft bound

Index